*purposeful design*

# Science

## Level Two

student
booklets

Purposeful Design Publications is the publishing division of the Association of Christian Schools International (ACSI) and is committed to the ministry of Christian school education, to enable Christian educators and schools worldwide to effectively prepare students for life. As the publisher of textbooks, trade books, and other educational resources within ACSI, Purposeful Design Publications strives to produce biblically sound materials that reflect Christian scholarship and stewardship and that address the identified needs of Christian schools around the world.

References to books, computer software, and other ancillary resources in this series are not endorsements by ACSI. These materials were selected to provide teachers with additional resources appropriate to the concepts being taught and to promote student understanding and enjoyment.

Unless otherwise identified, all Scripture quotations are taken from the Holy Bible, NEW INTERNATIONAL VERSION® (NIV®), © 1973, 1978, 1984 by International Bible Society. All rights reserved worldwide.

Photograph of George Washington Carver in Lesson 1.7 is in Public Domain. It is used according to the specifications of the Library of Congress, Prints and Photographs Division, Washington D.C. 20540. Reproduction number: LC–J601–302.
Picture of Smokey Bear in Lesson 4.9 is used by permission of the U.S. Forest Service and is the sole property of the U.S. Forest Service.
Photograph of Helen Keller in Lesson 9.4 is in Public Domain. It is used according to the specifications of the Library of Congress, Prints and Photographs Division, Washington D.C. 20540. Reproduction number: LC–USZ62–68302.
Photograph of the Great Barrier Reef in Lesson 12.7 is used courtesy of the Great Barrier Reef Marine Park Authority © GBRMPA.
Photograph of ALVIN in Lesson 12.8 is used by permission of OAR/National Undersea Research Program (NURP); Woods Hole Oceanographic Institution and is part of the NOAA Photo Library.
Photograph of PHANTOM S2 in Lesson 12.8 is used by permission of OAR/National Undersea Research Program (NURP); Woods Hole Oceanographic Institution and is part of the NOAA Photo Library.
FRISBEE® is a trademark of Wham-O Inc, which does not sponsor, authorize, or endorse this textbook.
LEGO® is a trademark of the LEGO Group of companies, which does not sponsor, authorize, or endorse this textbook.
TINKERTOY® is a trademark of Hasbro, which does not sponsor, authorize, or endorse this textbook.
STYROFOAM® is a trademark of the The Dow Chemical Company, which does not sponsor, authorize, or endorse this textbook.

Printed in the United States of America
17 16 15 14 13     8 9 10 11 12

*Purposeful Design Science, level two*
Purposeful Design Science series
ISBN 978-1-58331-205-6 Student edition Catalog #7505

Purposeful Design Publications
*A Division of ACSI*
PO Box 65130 • Colorado Springs, CO 80962-5130
Customer Service: 800-367-0798 • www.acsi.org

# purposeful design
# Science
## Level Two

**student booklets**

### Executive Editor
Derek Keenan

### Editorial Director
Steven Babbitt

### Managing Editors
John Conaway
Anita Gordon

### Editing Team
Bonnie Church
Stephen Johnson
Vanessa Rough
Kara Underwood

### Design Team
Susanna Garmany
Kris Orr
Dan Schultz
Sarah Schultz
Chris Tschamler

purposeful design
p u b l i c a t i o n s
A Division of ACSI
Colorado Springs, Colorado

# purposeful design
# Science

*Purposeful Design Publications is deeply grateful to the faculty and staff of Briarwood Christian School in Birmingham, Alabama, for the valuable and insightful contributions they have made to the structure and content of the Purposeful Design Science series.*

# Table of Contents

# Finding Answers to Science Questions

When scientists want to solve problems or answer questions about the natural world, they use the scientific method. To use the scientific method, follow these steps:

## 1. State the problem.

What question do you want to answer?

"Which cup will keep liquid hot longer?"

## 2. Form a hypothesis.

A hypothesis is a prediction or statement that can be tested to tell whether it is true. What do I think is the answer to my question?

"I think the foam cup will keep the liquid hot longer."

## 3. Plan a way to test the hypothesis.

What experiment will show whether my prediction is correct?

## 4. Test the hypothesis.

Do the experiment.

## 5. Collect and analyze the data.

Record the results of the experiment.
Organize the information.

|  | Initial temperature | Temperature after 10 minutes | Temperature after 20 minutes | Temperature after 30 minutes |
|---|---|---|---|---|
| Foam cup | 65° C |  |  |  |
| Ceramic mug | 65° C |  |  |  |

## 6. Draw conclusions and communicate results.

Was my hypothesis correct?
Has my question been
answered? Do I need to do
another experiment? How can
I show the results of my
experiment?

"My hypothesis was correct."

Plants provide us with food.

# My Booklet about Plants

**Name**

Draw your favorite plant.

We know that God made plants.

*Then God said, "Let the land produce vegetation: seed-bearing plants and trees on the land that bear fruit with seed in it, according to their various kinds."*

*Genesis 1:11*

Why did God make plants? He created plants to provide people and animals with the things they need.

Choose an example from the Word Bank that shows each of God's provisions.

**Fibers**

**Shelter**

_____

_____

**Food**

**Beauty**

_____

_____

| **Word Bank** | rose | paper | peanut | house |
|---|---|---|---|---|

Botany is the study of plants.

A botanist is a person who studies plants.

What might botanists do with what they learn about plants?

Fill in the circle next to the items that come from plants.

○    ○    ○

○    ○    ○

God made plants to meet our needs and to make us happy. He wants us to remember Him when we look at plants and to give Him praise. _____

-------------------------------------------

I thank God for plants because _____

_____

-------------------------------------------

_____

Most plants begin as seeds.

Seeds have three main parts: seed coat, tiny plant, and food.

Even though seeds are small, God designed them with everything they need to grow into a full-sized plant. A seed is the first stage in a plant's life cycle. A life cycle is the stages in the life of a plant or animal.

seed coat

food

tiny plant

Draw arrows to order the stages of a plant's life cycle.

Start

# How are seeds spread?

Some seeds are specially designed to be blown by the wind.

Some seeds are moved when they attach to an animal's coat or are eaten by an animal.

Some seeds are moved by floating in water.

Some seeds are spread when their pods burst open.

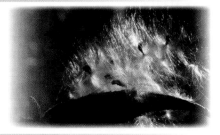

Guess how each seed is spread. Circle your guess.

| Coconut | Maple | Cherry |
| --- | --- | --- |
|  | | |
| wind   water   animal | wind   water   animal | wind   water   animal |

Plants make their own food. Their leaves are like tiny kitchens.

Photosynthesis is the way a plant makes food in its leaves.

When you want to make cookies, you have to get all the ingredients you need.

God designed plants so that they have all the ingredients they need.

light

water

Plants need four ingredients to make food.

chlorophyll

air

Circle the ingredients a plant needs to make food.

flour    light    air    milk    water    eggs    chlorophyll

# What Plants Need to Grow

Draw pictures of things that remind you of what plants need to grow.

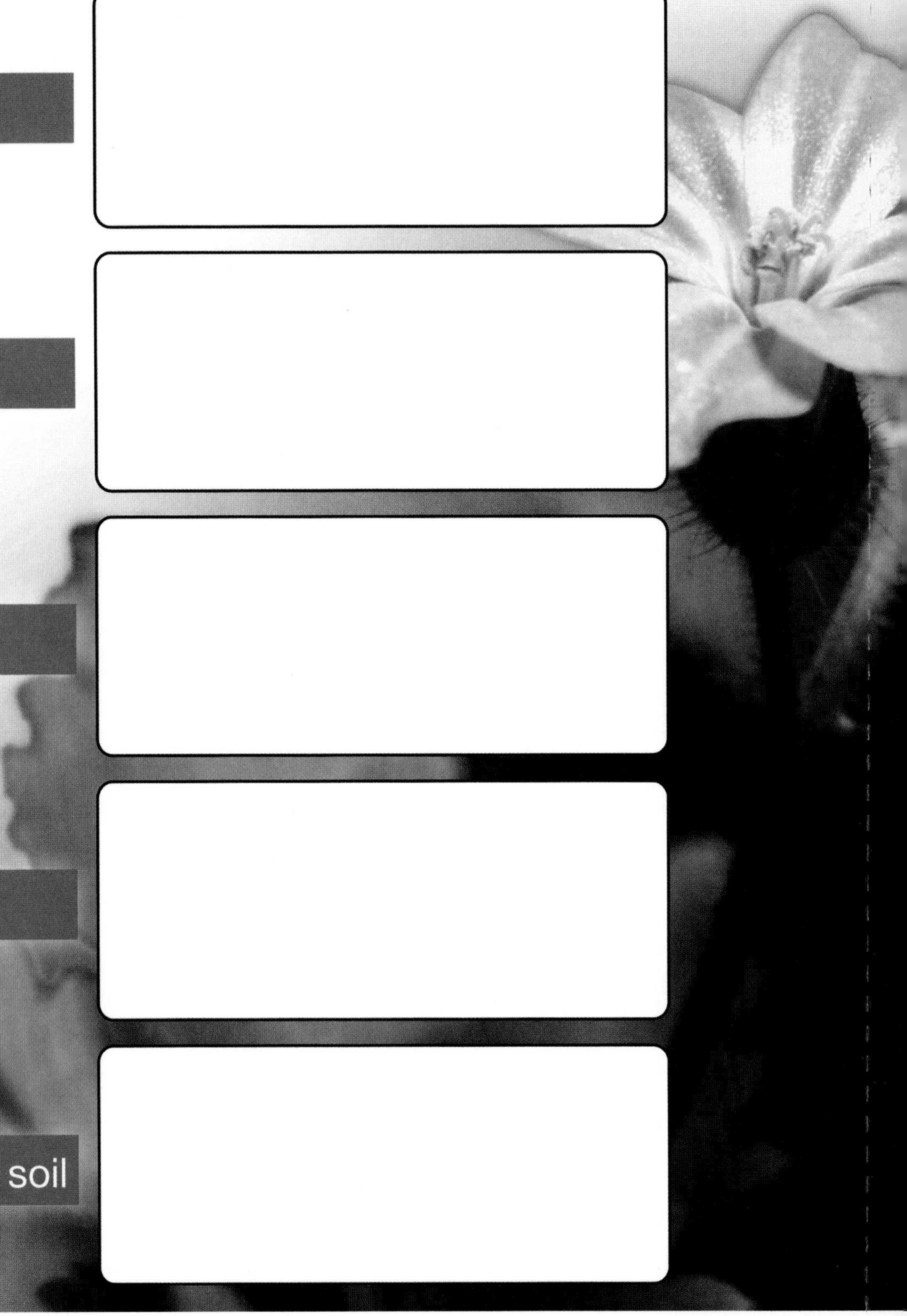

| Light | |
| Warmth | |
| Air | |
| Water | |
| Nutrients from soil | |

Use the Word Bank to label the three plant parts.

**Word Bank**
roots
leaves
stem

Use the Word Bank to complete the sentences.

The _____ absorb water and nutrients from the soil.

The _____ carries water and nutrients to the leaves.

The _____ make food for the plant.

## Make a plant model.

You will need a straw, three pieces of string, tape, scissors, green markers or crayons, and leaf shapes.

Follow the steps:

1. Tape three strings to one end of the straw to represent roots.

2. Color the leaf shapes green.

3. Cut them out and tape them to the straw which represents the stem.

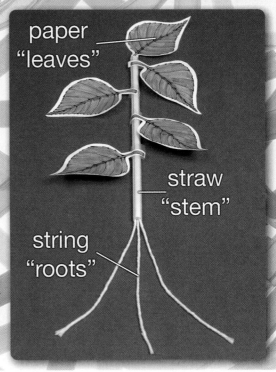

paper "leaves"

straw "stem"

string "roots"

On the lines below, write how a plant moves water and nutrients from the soil to its leaves.

*The land produced vegetation: plants bearing seed according to their kinds and trees bearing fruit with seed in it according to their kinds. And God saw that it was good.  Genesis 1:12*

God designed some plants with seeds.
Flowering plants have flowers that produce seeds.

Seeds are formed in the base of the flower.

This part grows into a fruit that protects the seeds.

An apple blossom becomes the apple, which holds the apple seeds.

Draw a line from the flower to the fruit it becomes.

orange blossom

cherry blossom

strawberry blossom

Some plants make seeds in cones.
These plants are called conifers.

**pine cone**

These trees are examples of conifers.

**Pine Trees**

**Cedar Trees**

Did you know that redwoods
are the tallest trees on earth?

**Redwood Trees**

Seeds form inside the
cone. When the cone opens, its seeds are
scattered by the wind, water, or animals.

What is the difference between a conifer and a
flowering plant?

_____

_____

_____

_____

Use the Word Bank to complete the chart.

| Plant Part | Example | Plant Part's Job |
|---|---|---|
| _____ | | They soak up water and nutrients from the soil. |
| _____ | | They carry water and nutrients from the roots to the leaves. |
| _____ | | They make food for the plant. |
| _____ | | They make fruit to hold the seeds. |
| _____ | | They hold the seeds. |
| _____ | | They are planted in the ground to grow new plants. |

**Word Bank**   leaves   fruit   roots   stems   seeds   flowers

© 2005

**13**

*Then God said, "I give you every seed-bearing plant on the face of the whole earth and every tree that has fruit with seed in it. They will be yours for food." Genesis 1:29*

God made many different kinds of plants so people and animals could have many delicious foods to choose from!

God designed plants to store important vitamins and minerals that help us stay healthy.

When we eat these foods, we help our bodies to fight sickness and grow stronger.

Draw a line from each picture to the name of the plant part.

Leaf

Root

Stem

Seed

Fruit

Flower

# History Connect

George Washington Carver was born a slave. He taught himself how to read because he loved to learn.

He went to college and studied plants. As a scientist, he wanted to help people with what he learned about plants.

**The Problem:** In the southern United States, farmers had planted cotton for 200 years. The cotton plants had used up all the nutrients in the soil.

**The Solution:** George Washington Carver came up with the idea to rotate crops. If cotton was planted one year, peanuts, soybeans, or sweet potatoes would be planted the next.

These plants returned the nutrients to the soil that the cotton plants used up. Use the Word Bank to show how farmers can rotate crops each year.

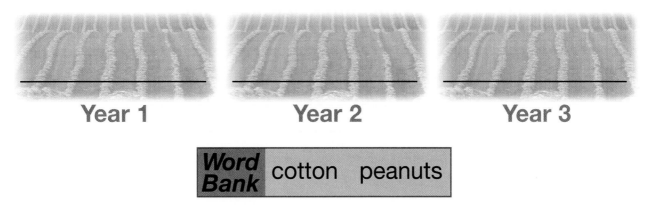

Year 1   Year 2   Year 3

**Word Bank** cotton peanuts

**New Problem:** Soon farmers were producing more peanuts than they knew what to do with!

**Solution:** George Washington Carver discovered over 300 new uses for peanuts.

He found a way to make ink, cooking oil, and even shampoo out of peanuts.

George Washington Carver did not try to make money from his ideas. He said, "God gave them to me, how can I sell them to someone else?"

Thomas Edison offered him $100,000 to work for him, but Carver refused. He wanted to continue to improve the lives of poor people through his discoveries.

What gifts and talents has God given you?

_____

- - - - - - - - - - - - - - - - - - - - - - - - - - - - - - - -

_____

How can you help others with your talents?

_____

- - - - - - - - - - - - - - - - - - - - - - - - - - - - - - - -

_____

- - - - - - - - - - - - - - - - - - - - - - - - - - - - - - - -

_____

**1.** Circle the things that plants must have to grow.

gardener     light and warmth     animals     air

water     container     nutrients     shovel

**2.** In the boxes, draw two things that come from plants.

**3.** Write the names of two plants that produce fruit.

_____     _____

Fill in the circle next to the word that completes each sentence.

1. Plants make food in their _____ .
   ○ leaves          ○ stems

2. Seeds are scattered by wind, water, and _____ .
   ○ soil            ○ animals

3. A conifer has _____ that hold its seeds.
   ○ cones           ○ flowers

4. A botanist studies _____ .
   ○ plants          ○ animals

# Journal about Plants

Write two things you learned about plants.

_____

_____

_____

_____

_____

_____

_____

Dogs can make good pets.

# My Booklet about Vertebrates

Name _____

Color.

reptile

mammal

fish

bird

amphibian

*And God said, "Let the water teem with living creatures, and let birds fly above the earth across the expanse of the sky.... Let the land produce living creatures according to their kinds: livestock, creatures that move along the ground, and wild animals, each according to its kind." Genesis 1:20, 24*

God created animals with unique designs for specific purposes. Unique means one of a kind. There is no one or nothing else just the same.

A vertebrate is an animal with a backbone. God designed vertebrates to be able to walk, run, sit, leap, and crawl. A backbone gives vertebrates the ability to move and bend in many different directions. This design helps them to gather food, protect themselves, and sleep.

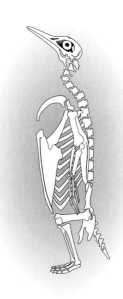

| Amazing Animal Fact | Amazing Animal Fact | Amazing Animal Fact | Amazing Animal Fact |
|---|---|---|---|
| Angel fish can lay hundreds of eggs at one time. | Owls cannot move their eyes in their sockets, so they must turn their heads to see a moving object. | The sea horse uses its tail to hold on to rooted plants under the sea | Robins usually return to the same place each year to build their nests. |

Scientists classify animals by sorting them into groups based on similarities and differences.

Vertebrates are classified as mammals, birds, reptiles, fish, or amphibians.

Birds are warm-blooded vertebrates with feathers, wings, and two feet. They have beaks instead of teeth.

The body temperature of a warm-blooded animal does not change much with the outside temperature.

Fish are cold-blooded vertebrates that use gills to breathe. Most are covered with scales and have fins to swim.

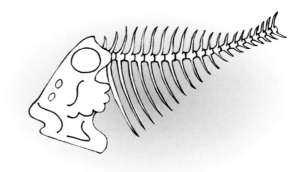

The body temperature of a cold-blooded animal changes with the outside temperature.

Cut out the cards. Classify each animal as a fish or bird.

A vertebrate is an animal with a backbone. Vertebrates are classified as mammals, birds, reptiles, fish, or amphibians.

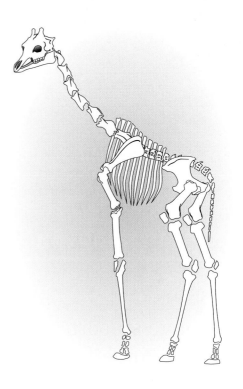

Mammals are warm-blooded vertebrates that have hair. They make milk for their babies. They have lungs to breathe air.

The body temperature of a warm-blooded animal does not change much with the outside temperature.

Name each animal. Which animals are mammals?

Reptiles are cold-blooded vertebrates that have dry, scaly skin. They have lungs to breathe. The body temperature of a cold-blooded animal changes with the outside temperature. Which animal cards show reptiles?

Amphibians are cold-blooded vertebrates that have smooth, moist skin. Their bodies change form as they grow. Which animal cards show amphibians?

Read the amazing animal facts. Cut out the cards. Classify each animal as a mammal, reptile, or amphibian.

| Amazing Animal Fact | Amazing Animal Fact | Amazing Animal Fact | Amazing Animal Fact |
|---|---|---|---|
| A turtle's backbone is under its shell. | Most frogs have long back legs that help them jump. | A chameleon changes color if it is frightened. | Elephants are the largest animals that live on land. |
| **Amazing Animal Fact** | **Amazing Animal Fact** | **Amazing Animal Fact** | **Amazing Animal Fact** |
| Bats are the only mammals that can fly. | Snakes use their tongues to smell their prey. | If a salamander loses its tail, it can grow a new one! | Whales have lungs and come to the surface to breathe. |

# What is a mammal?

## A mammal...

- **has a backbone**
- **is warm-blooded**
- **has hair**

- **can make milk to feed its young**
- **has lungs to breathe**

God gave animals different abilities. People can train dogs to do special tasks. Use the Word Bank to match the kind of dog with the task.

| **Word Bank** | police | guide |
|---|---|---|
| | herder | rescue |

Border collies are used on ranches to keep a flock of sheep together.

_____

German shepherds are used to track criminals and find drugs and explosives.

_____

St. Bernards are used in cold, mountain areas to help find lost people.

_____

Labrador retrievers are used as seeing-eye dogs that help visually-impaired people.

_____

Fill in the circle next to the correct answer.

A cat's ____ feels like sandpaper. It is used for grooming.

○ paws          ○ tail          ○ tongue

A cat's ____ are very sensitive and can feel the slightest touch. It helps the cat determine the width of spaces.

○ eyes          ○ whiskers          ○ teeth

A cat uses its ____ to keep its balance.

○ tail          ○ nose          ○ fur

This cat is known as a Ragdoll. How do you think the cat got its name?

Use the Word Bank to complete each sentence.

Guinea pigs gnaw on _____ to keep their teeth short.

Guinea pigs make different _____ when they are happy, angry, or hungry.

They like to eat _____ , fruit, and hay.

Guinea pigs can live to be _____ years old.

| Word Bank |
|---|
| nine |
| sounds |
| wood |
| vegetables |

# What is a reptile?

## A reptile...

- **has a backbone**
- **is cold-blooded**
- **has dry, scaly skin**

- **lays eggs on dry land**
- **breathes with lungs**

Fill in the blanks to complete the sentences about iguanas.

Iguanas can be found in many different places including rain forests, _____ , and by the sea.

Iguanas can be _____ , brown, yellow, or white.

Iguanas eat mostly _____ .

If it is caught, an iguana's _____ can break off, but it will grow back.

Iguanas can dive into the water and _____ away from predators.

Some iguanas grow to over _____ feet long.

| **Word** | green | tail | swim |
| **Bank** | deserts | six | plants |

Use the Word Bank to label the iguana.

**Word Bank**

| dorsal crests | nostril | long tail |
|---|---|---|
| scaly skin | dewlap | clawed foot |

# What is an amphibian?

### An amphibian...

- has a backbone
- is cold-blooded
- has smooth, moist skin
- lays eggs in or around water

- breathes with gills until it develops lungs
- goes through metamorphosis

Metamorphosis means a change of form. Amphibians change their form as they grow into adults.

A life cycle is the stages in the life of a plant or animal.

Young salamanders look very different from their parents. They go through many changes to become adults.

The larvae use gills to breathe.

Salamanders begin as eggs.

Adult salamanders have lungs. Females lay eggs.

Here are some amphibians you may know.

toad

frog

salamander

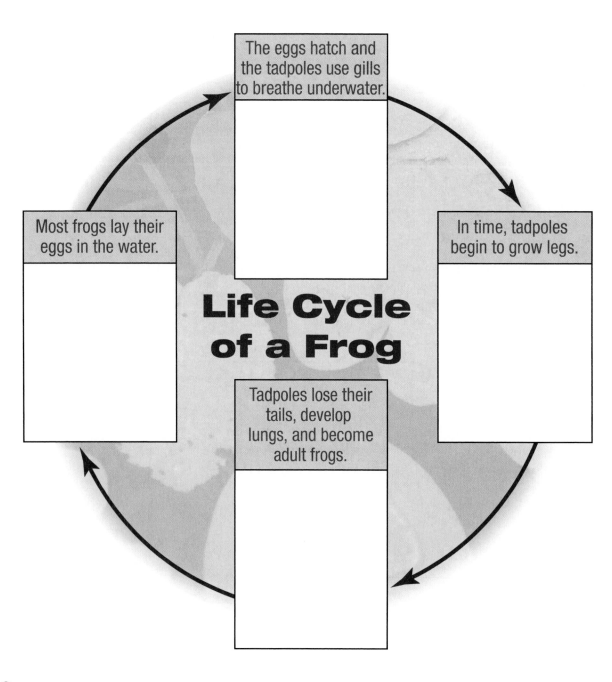

The eggs hatch and the tadpoles use gills to breathe underwater.

Most frogs lay their eggs in the water.

In time, tadpoles begin to grow legs.

# Life Cycle of a Frog

Tadpoles lose their tails, develop lungs, and become adult frogs.

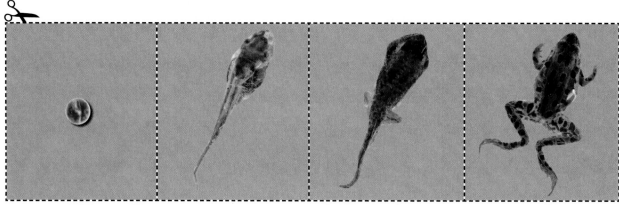

Camels are called "the ships of the desert" because they transport people and heavy loads. Both legs on one side of the camel's body move forward and then both legs on the other side move forward. As it walks, it rocks back and forth like a ship.

God gave this mammal a very special body to help it live in the desert. Use the Word Bank to complete the sentences.

**Word Bank** face feet neck body legs hump

The _____ stores food for the camel to use when food is in short supply.

The parts of the _____ work together to protect the camel.

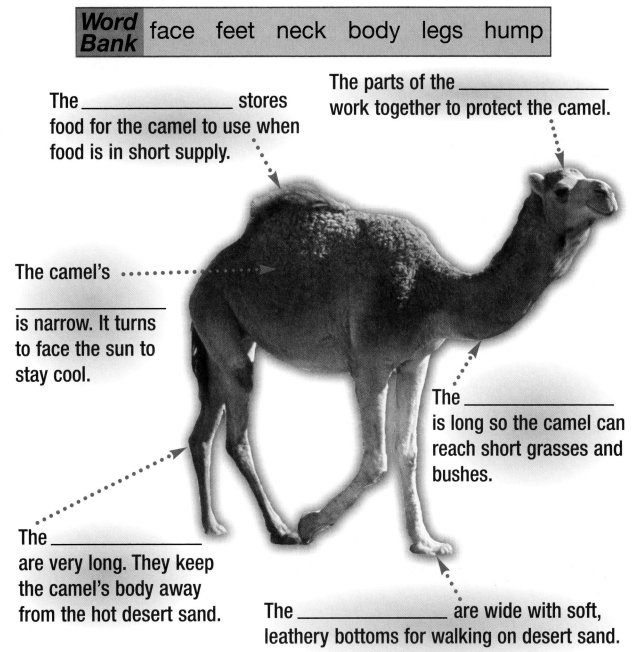

The camel's _____ is narrow. It turns to face the sun to stay cool.

The _____ is long so the camel can reach short grasses and bushes.

The _____ are very long. They keep the camel's body away from the hot desert sand.

The _____ are wide with soft, leathery bottoms for walking on desert sand.

Arabian Camel

- An Arabian camel has one hump.

- One type of Arabian camel is called a dromedary. It is used for racing and riding.

- An Arabian camel has shorter fur because it lives in warmer climates.

- A Bactrian camel has two humps.

- It has longer fur because it lives in colder climates.

Bactrian Camel

- The fur of a Bactrian camel is woven into cloth to make blankets, suits, and coats.

Name one way an Arabian camel and a Bactrian camel are different.

_____

- - - - - - - - - - - - - - - - - - - - - - - - - - - - - - - - - - - - -

_____

## Crazy Camel Facts

- A camel has three stomachs. Each holds five gallons of water. How many gallons of water can one camel hold?

_____

- People drink milk from a camel. They also make cheese from camel milk. What other animal gives us milk to drink?

_____

# History Connect

Artist Painting

John James Audubon was a famous artist in the 1800s who painted pictures of birds and wildlife. He enjoyed learning about animals and where they live. Before he began to paint, he would observe the birds and write down what he saw in a notebook. To observe is to watch carefully with attention to detail.

Observe the picture. Name three details you need to remember to draw the picture.

1. _____

2. _____

3. _____

Observe this picture and write two details to remember.

1. _____

2. _____

 At age 18, John James Audubon moved to America. He became one of the first people to paint lifelike pictures of birds. His paintings became famous and valuable.

Observe the following pictures and circle the one you want to draw. Study the photo carefully, then draw your picture.

Drawing by _____

A bird is a warm-blooded vertebrate that has feathers, wings, and two feet.

Fill in the circle next to the correct answer.

**1.** A vertebrate is an animal with a _____.
    ○ hoof        ○ backbone      ○ fin

**2.** Metamorphosis is when an animal's body goes through
    a _____ of form.
    ○ change      ○ adulthood     ○ habitat

**3.** The stages in the life of a plant or animal are called
    a _____.
    ○ clock        ○ vertebrate     ○ life cycle

## Metamorphosis

Number the life cycle stages of a frog in order from 1 to 4.

_____

_____

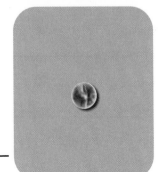

_____

_____

# Use the Word Bank to fill in the blanks.

Giraffe

Rainbow trout

Owl

_____    _____    _____

Rattlesnake

**Word Bank**

reptile
bird
fish
mammal
amphibian

Frog

_____    _____

# Journal about Vertebrates

Write about your favorite vertebrate.

_____

- - - - - - - - - - - - - - - - - - - - - - - - - - - - - - - - - - - - - - - -

_____

_____

- - - - - - - - - - - - - - - - - - - - - - - - - - - - - - - - - - - - - - - -

_____

_____

_____

- - - - - - - - - - - - - - - - - - - - - - - - - - - - - - - - - - - - - - - -

_____

A spider makes a web.

# My Booklet about Invertebrates

**Name** _____

Draw a spider. How many legs does it have?

God designed some animals without backbones. They are called invertebrates.

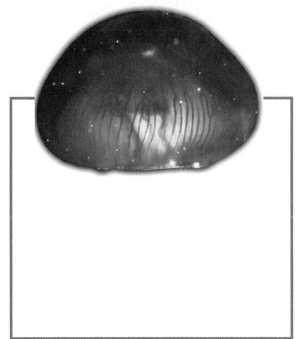

Jellyfish have tentacles that sting to help them catch food.

Draw the tentacles.

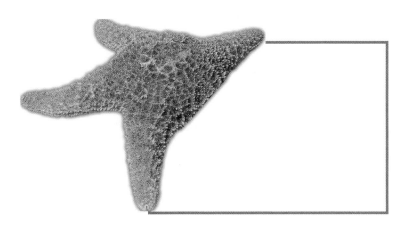

A starfish can regrow its arm if it is broken off.

Draw the arm.

Slugs leave a trail of mucus behind when they crawl. The mucus helps them slide and protects them from rough surfaces in their path.

Draw the trail of mucus.

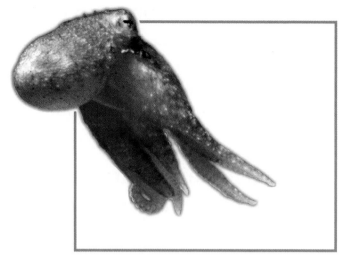

An octopus can squirt a black fluid to make a cloud that helps it hide from sharks, whales, and other enemies.

Draw the black cloud.

Butterflies have antennae that help them smell. This is how they find food.

Draw the antennae.

Write about an invertebrate that you have seen.

**Materials**

foam plate
small cup of water
3 or 4 earthworms
craft stick
hand lens
eyedropper
black construction paper

**Skills**

predict
observe

**Problem**    How do earthworms behave?

A hypothesis is a prediction or statement that can be tested to tell if it is true.

**Hypothesis**    I think earthworms move in _____ lines.
○ straight    ○ wiggly

I think earthworms like a _____ surface better.
○ dry          ○ wet

I think earthworms like _____ better.
○ light          ○ darkness

**Plan**    How can you test each hypothesis?

**Experiment**    Observe the demonstration.

**Observe and Collect Data**

The earthworms move in a _____ line.
○ straight   ○ wiggly

The earthworms like a _____ surface better.
○ dry        ○ wet

The earthworms like _____ better.
○ light      ○ darkness

**Conclusion**

Decide if each hypothesis you made was correct.

Write what you learned about earthworms.

_____

- - - - - - - - - - - - - - - - - - - - - - - - - - - - - - -

_____

_____

- - - - - - - - - - - - - - - - - - - - - - - - - - - - - - -

_____

_____

- - - - - - - - - - - - - - - - - - - - - - - - - - - - - - -

_____

_____

- - - - - - - - - - - - - - - - - - - - - - - - - - - - - - -

_____

_____

- - - - - - - - - - - - - - - - - - - - - - - - - - - - - - -

_____

Many people think spiders are insects, but scientists classify them separately.

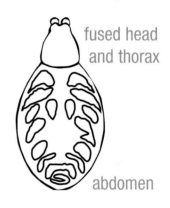

Spiders have eight legs, while insects have six.

Most insects have wings and antennae, but spiders do not.

Their bodies are different. Spiders have two parts, and insects have three.

Complete the drawings below.

**For the spider. . .**
- Draw eight legs.
- Draw two fangs.

fused head and thorax

abdomen

head

thorax

abdomen

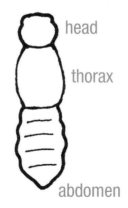

**For the insect. . .**
- Draw six legs.
- Draw two antennae.
- Draw two wings.

*Color your spider and your insect.*

God designed spiders with many special features.

Spiders spin webs to catch insects for food.

All spiders have fangs, and some have venom that can kill insects and small animals that they eat for food.

Some spiders can harm people. One example is a female black widow. It has a red or yellow hourglass shape on its abdomen.

Spiders are helpful to people because they eat harmful insects.

Write about a spider you have seen.

_____

--------------------------------------

_____

--------------------------------------

_____

--------------------------------------

_____

Ants are social insects that live and work with other ants.

They live in large groups called colonies.

Ants do not have lungs. God designed them with small breathing holes on their sides called spiracles.

Draw a line from the word to the correct body part.

**antennae**

These are used to taste, touch, smell, and hear.

**mandibles**

These jaws are used for eating, as tools for making tunnels, and as weapons.

**spiracles**

These are air tubes that ants use to breathe.

**sting**

Some ants have a sting at the end of their body. They can use this against enemies.

Even though ants are small, they are very strong. Some ants can lift objects 10 times heavier than they are.

That would be the same as you lifting 10 of your friends!

The Bible mentions the ant several times and praises it for being wise.

*Four things on earth are small, yet they are extremely wise: Ants are creatures of little strength, yet they store up their food in the summer.*

*Proverbs 30:24–25*

_____

- - - - - - - - - - - - - - - - - - - - - - - - - - - - - - - - -

The Bible says ants are wise because _____

- - - - - - - - - - - - - - - - - - - - - - - - - - - - - - - - - - - - - - - - - - - - - - - - - - - - - - -

_____

What other lesson can we learn from ants?

_____

- - - - - - - - - - - - - - - - - - - - - - - - - - - - - - - - - - - - - - - - - - - - - - - - - - - - - - -

_____

- - - - - - - - - - - - - - - - - - - - - - - - - - - - - - - - - - - - - - - - - - - - - - - - - - - - - - -

_____

_____

- - - - - - - - - - - - - - - - - - - - - - - - - - - - - - - - - - - - - - - - - - - - - - - - - - - - - - -

_____

Snails belong to a group of animals called mollusks.

Mollusks are soft-bodied invertebrates that usually have shells. Clams, snails, and scallops are mollusks. Other mollusks, like slugs, do not have shells. Octopuses and squid are also mollusks.

Read about the snail and color each part.

The shell protects the snail.

The foot helps the snail move.

Eyespots help the snail see.

The tentacles help the snail feel things.

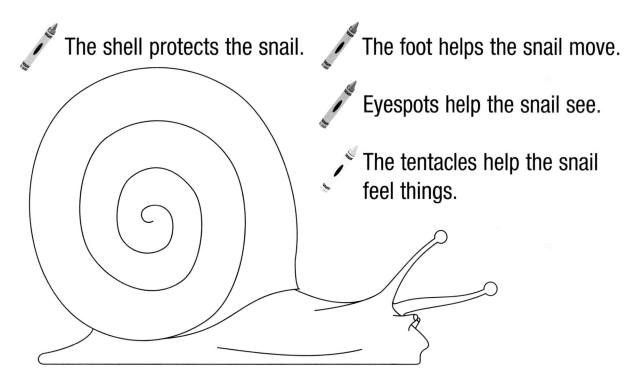

Snails release a sticky liquid called mucus. This helps them slide along the ground.

Snails are an important food for many fish and birds.

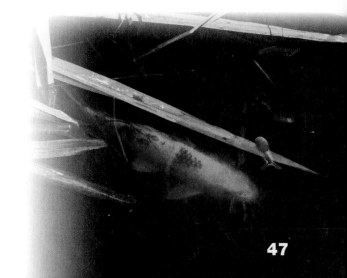

Use the Word Bank to write the words that describe snails.

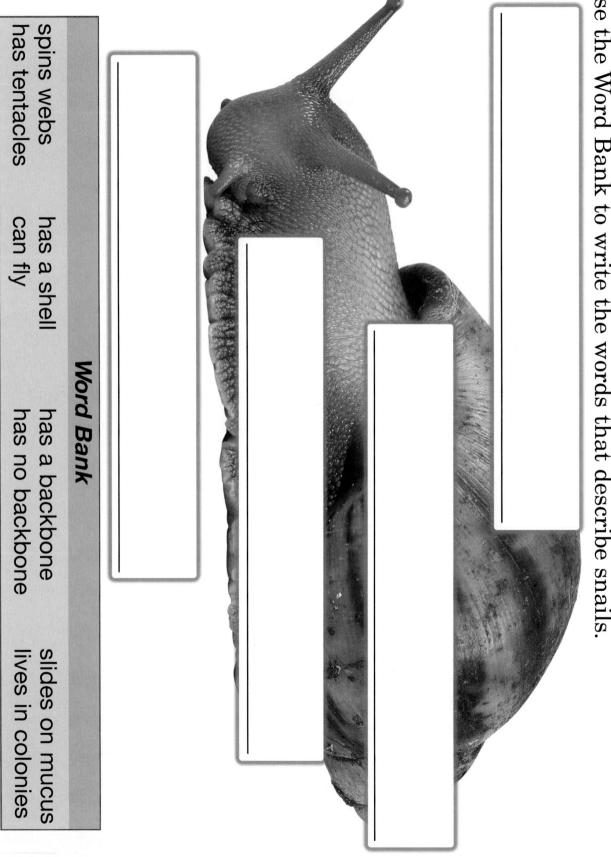

**Word Bank**

| | | |
|---|---|---|
| spins webs | has a shell | slides on mucus |
| has tentacles | can fly | lives in colonies |
| | has a backbone | |
| | has no backbone | |

Use the clues and the Word Bank to complete the crossword puzzle.

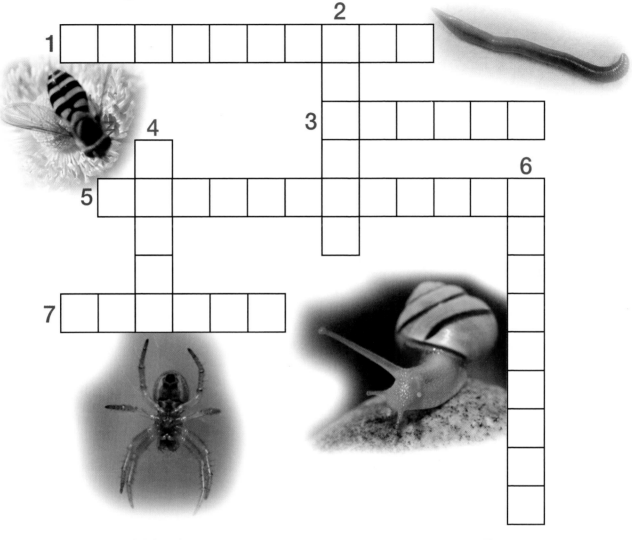

## Across

**1.** Prediction that can be tested

**3.** Has six legs

**5.** Animal without a backbone

**7.** A large group of ants that live and work together

## Down

**2.** Has eight legs

**4.** Has a hard shell

**6.** Animal that loosens soil

| **Word Bank** | earthworm | colony | invertebrate | hypothesis |
| | snail | insect | spider | |

Classify the following invertebrates.

1. I am a moth. I have six legs and three body sections. I have antennae and I fly. What am I?

   ○ insect    ○ spider    ○ worm    ○ mollusk

2. I am a clam. I have a hard shell. My body is soft and I have no bones. I live underwater. What am I?

   ○ insect    ○ spider    ○ worm    ○ mollusk

# Journal about Invertebrates

Write two things you learned about invertebrates.

_____

- - - - - - - - - - - - - - - - - - - - - - - - - - - - - - - -

_____

- - - - - - - - - - - - - - - - - - - - - - - - - - - - - - - -

_____

- - - - - - - - - - - - - - - - - - - - - - - - - - - - - - - -

_____

- - - - - - - - - - - - - - - - - - - - - - - - - - - - - - - -

_____

- - - - - - - - - - - - - - - - - - - - - - - - - - - - - - - -

_____

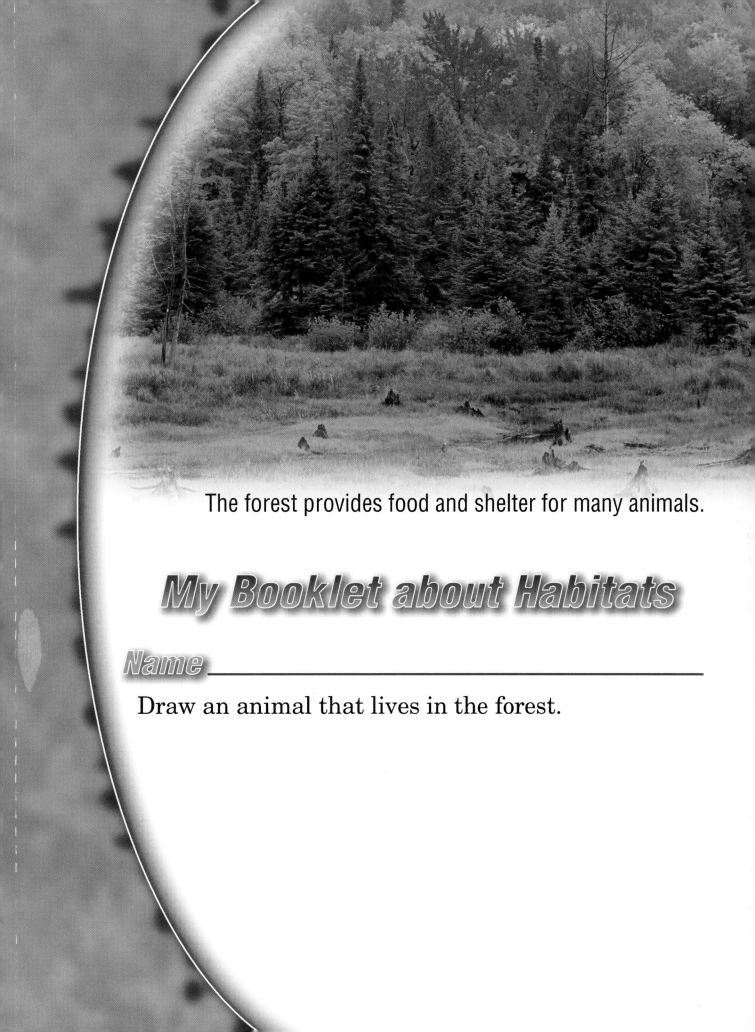

The forest provides food and shelter for many animals.

# My Booklet about Habitats

Name _____

Draw an animal that lives in the forest.

A habitat is a place where an animal lives, finds its food, and is sheltered.

Cut out each animal picture and glue it in the correct habitat.

*Does the eagle soar at your command and build his nest on high? He dwells on a cliff and stays there at night; a rocky crag (steep, rugged rock) is his stronghold. From there he seeks out his food; his eyes detect it from afar. Job 39: 27–29*

polar
bear

raccoon

sidewinder
rattlesnake

alligator

trout

toucan

**Forest**

**Freshwater**

**Wetland**

Examine the picture of this garden. There are many plants and animals that are found here. This is their habitat.

Name one place an animal might find shelter in the garden.

_____

- - - - - - - - - - - - - - - - - - - - - - - - - - -

_____

An animal needs food to live. Name one plant in this garden that an animal could eat.

_____

- - - - - - - - - - - - - - - - - - - - - - - - - - -

_____

Circle all the plants and animals that might be found in a yard or garden habitat.

© 2005

*These all look to you to give them their food at the proper time. When you give it to them, they gather it up; when you open your hand, they are satisfied with good things. Psalm 104: 27–28*

The order in which animals eat plants and other animals is called a food chain. The plant, the worm, and the bird are all part of the food chain in this habitat. The bird eats the worm. The bird is a predator. The worm is the food. It is the prey.

A forest habitat has enough rainfall for a thick growth of trees and plants. It is warm at least part of the year. There can be small ponds and streams in forests.

Can you describe a forest you have seen?

Draw something a bear finds in the forest to meet its needs.

Why is the forest a good habitat for this deer?

God designed the color and patterns of each animal and placed them in a habitat that was perfect for them. The color or pattern that helps an animal hide in its habitat is called camouflage.

Some animals use camouflage to hide from their enemies. What animal is hiding here?

_____

Some animals use camouflage to sneak up on animals they are hunting. What animal is hiding in this picture?

_____

Color the forest animals. Which ones are camouflaged?

Freshwater regions are habitat areas where there is little or no salt in the water. They include streams, rivers, ponds, and lakes. Use the Word Bank to label each region.

**Word Bank** | river stream pond lake

This moving freshwater habitat carries water to larger rivers. Few plants grow in the water.

_____

This moving freshwater habitat carries water to lakes and oceans. Plants grow along the banks.

_____

This still, freshwater habitat is smaller than a lake and has many plants that grow in and around it.

_____

This large, still, freshwater habitat is fed by rain and melting snow. Many plants grow here.

_____

A pond is a freshwater habitat. Many different types of plants grow here. Animals can find plenty of food and shelter to meet their needs.

Use the Word Bank to complete the chart showing where animals are usually found in the pond.

| In the water | On top of the water | Near the water's edge |
| --- | --- | --- |
| _____ | _____ | _____ |
| _____ | _____ | _____ |
| _____ | _____ | _____ |

### Word Bank

| | | |
| --- | --- | --- |
| deer | mosquito | fish |
| water strider | duck | tadpole |
| crayfish | beaver | raccoon |

Wetlands are habitats where the land is wet and soggy most of the year. Bogs, marshes, and swamps are all wetlands.

Bogs are located in cool climates. Their main source of water is rain. Many birds and insects live in a bog.

Marshes can form along rivers. They are filled with water when the rivers flood. Small, grassy plants and water lilies grow well in the water. Marshes provide food and shelter for many animals. Mosquitoes, dragonflies, frogs, and snakes live in marshes. The dragonflies eat mosquitoes, frogs eat dragonflies, and snakes eat frogs.

This is called a _____ _____.

Number the food chain in order from 1 to 4.

_____   __1__   _____   _____

Birds that migrate or travel from one place to another often stop in wetland areas to rest and find food. Name one bird that migrates to a warmer climate in the winter.

A swamp is drier than a marsh even though some parts of a swamp are flooded all year long. Certain trees and shrubs grow in swampy areas. It is home to many animals such as frogs, snakes, red-winged blackbirds, and mallards.

The Florida Everglades, in the United States, is a freshwater wetland. This is a natural habitat for many animals such as snowy egrets, white-tailed deer, dragonflies, and alligators.

Draw an alligator in the Florida Everglades.

Desert habitats receive very little rainfall and have harsh temperatures. Some get very hot during the day and very cold at night. Many types of plants and animals live in deserts.

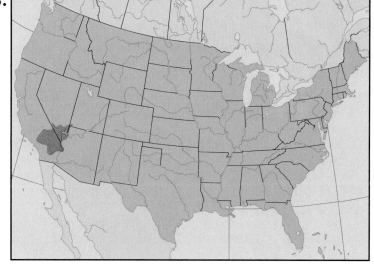

The Mojave Desert, located in the United States, is a hot, dry desert. Can you think of a reptile that lives in this desert?

This saguaro cactus can store water in its long stems. Why is this important for a desert plant?

The Cactus Wren makes its home inside a saguaro. Why is this a safe place to live?

Many desert animals are nocturnal. This means they sleep during the day and are active at night. Why does this help animals?

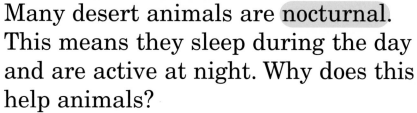

# Find the animals living in this desert and label them.

| Word Bank | | |
|---|---|---|
| cactus wren | roadrunner | lizard |
| rattlesnake | jackrabbit | coyote |

A polar region habitat has very cold temperatures. It is covered with ice and snow most of the year. Polar regions include the Arctic and Antarctica.

The Arctic
- Located near the North Pole
- Very cold with snow covering the ground most of the year
- Mainly ice-covered ocean surrounded by frozen land
- A place with a short summer when plants can grow
- A place for animals that are designed to live in the cold

| **Word Bank** | paws | fur | dens | seals | fat |
|---|---|---|---|---|---|

Polar bears have layers of _____ under their skin to keep them warm.

Their heavy _____ also keeps them warm.

Polar bears eat mostly _____.

In the winter, mother polar bears live in snow _____ where they give birth to their cubs.

A polar bear's large _____ act like snowshoes.

## Antarctica

- Located at the South Pole
- The coldest region on earth
- Mainly ice-covered land surrounded by the ocean
- A place where very few land animals live
- A wide variety of animal life in and around the sea

Antarctica

| **Word Bank** | Emperor   fish   white   rookery |
| --- | --- |

Penguins eat krill, squid, and _____.

The place a group of penguins nest and raise their young is a _____.

The _____ penguin stands about four feet tall and is the largest penguin.

A penguin's chest is _____ to help it look like a floating iceberg in the water.

Tropical rain forests are located in the dark green areas of this map. Locate your country and find the closest tropical rain forest.

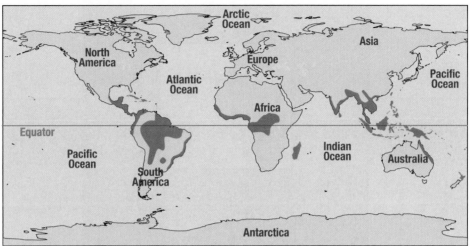

## Tropical Rain Forests

- Warm and humid all year
- Receive a large amount of rain
- Home to almost one-half of all the earth's animals
- Produce nuts, coffee, cocoa, bananas, pineapples, and many other foods

Cut out the pictures. Glue each one on the correct clue given on the next page.

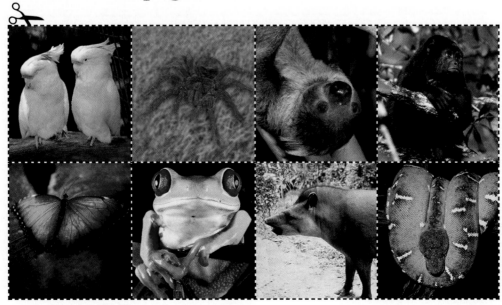

glue

I am blue. I drink the juice from rotting fruit.

glue

I have sticky toe pads that help me hang on the underside of tree leaves.

glue

I spend most of my time hanging upside down in trees. I am furry and slow-moving.

glue

I live in the trees and fly from branch to branch looking for nuts and berries to eat.

glue

I walk on the forest floor looking for plants and fruit to eat.

glue

I hang from trees and kill my prey by squeezing it.

glue

I live high in the trees and make howling noises. I eat leaves.

glue

I eat insects, frogs, lizards, and snakes. I have eight legs.

*The earth is the LORD's, and everything in it,*
*the world, and all who live in it. Psalm 24:1*

We need to take care of our environment and not pollute it. Pollute means to make things so dirty or unclean that it is harmful to life.

The air we breathe needs to be clean. Exhaust fumes from cars and trucks pollute our air. Polluted air can make people and animals very sick.

I can help keep the air clean by

_____

- - - - - - - - - - - - - - - - - - - - - - - - - - - - - - - - - - - - - - - - - - - -

_____

The land where we live needs to be clean. Trash that is not thrown away in proper containers can become harmful to animals. Plants cannot grow.

I can help keep the land clean by

_____

- - - - - - - - - - - - - - - - - - - - - - - - - - - - - - - - - - - - - - - - - - - -

_____

The water we drink needs to be clean. Chemicals and garbage that are put into the water can pollute it. What can you do to help keep the water clean?

© 2005

Do your part to help the environment by remembering the three Rs—reduce, reuse, recycle.

Reduce means to use less of something and not waste what you have. Have you ever used two paper towels when one was enough?

Reuse means to use something again. Name something you can use again.

Recycle means to make new material from old ones. What does your family recycle?

Write *yes* or *no* on the blank to tell if this is a good thing to do to help the environment.

_____ Throwing trash in proper containers

_____ Putting plastic containers in lakes

_____ Playing with matches

_____ Planting a tree in the yard

When there are very few animals of a certain kind living they are called endangered. This means they are close to being extinct or no longer living.

Animals do not always become extinct when they are listed as endangered. Some animals are moved to the threatened list when their numbers increase.

Once, over 40 million American bison, or buffalo, roamed the open prairies. In less than 100 years, almost all of them were gone due to over-hunting.

The buffalo was placed on the endangered list and protected by law. This helped their numbers to grow at a rapid rate. Today ranchers raise buffalo in the same way as cattle.

Giant pandas live in the forests and mountains of China. They eat mostly bamboo. When bamboo plants are cut down or destroyed the pandas lose their source of food. Giant pandas are listed as endangered because there are so few of them.

Draw a line from the event to the animal it directly affected.

Overhunting for food and clothing

Loss of natural food source due to bamboo plants being cut down

Oil spills coating the animal's fur

Poison on seagrass caused by red tide

Write about how you would feel if there were no more pandas.

_____

- - - - - - - - - - - - - - - - - - - - - - - - - - - - - - - - - - - - - - -

_____

- - - - - - - - - - - - - - - - - - - - - - - - - - - - - - - - - - - - - - -

_____

Draw a line to match the habitat to its description.

**1.** Desert

**2.** Forest

**3.** Tropical rain forest

**4.** Wetland

**5.** Polar region

**6.** Freshwater region

- It is very cold most of the year. In the Arctic and Antarctica, the land and water are covered with ice. Penguins live in Antarctica.

- It has a hot, dry climate with very little rainfall. Lizards live here.

- The land is mainly water-soaked and soggy. Bogs, marshes, and swamps are all types of this habitat. Alligators may live here.

- This area contains little or no salt in the water. Streams, rivers, ponds, and lakes are all types of this habitat. Trout live here.

- It is warm and humid all year. It receives a large amount of rain. Toucans live here.

- It gets enough rainfall for a thick growth of trees and plants. It is warm at least part of the year. Deer live here.

Fill in the circle next to the correct answer.

1. Camouflage is a color or pattern that helps an animal _____ in its habitat.

   ○ breathe          ○ hide          ○ run

2. Pandas are _____ animals that need to be protected.

   ○ dangerous        ○ extinct       ○ endangered

3. Not disposing of trash properly can pollute our ____.

   ○ water            ○ wind          ○ fire

4. When you _____ something you are making something new out of something old.

   ○ reduce           ○ reuse         ○ recycle

# ═Journal about Habitats═

Write about one animal and its habitat.

_____

_____

_____

_____

_____

_____

_____

_____

Energy makes things work.

# My Booklet about Energy

Name _____

Draw something you do that takes energy.

*In the beginning God created the heavens and the earth.*
*Genesis 1:1*

God is powerful and mighty. When He created the universe, He created it with an enormous amount of energy. God filled the earth with light and warmth and all kinds of sounds.

God gave us wisdom to learn how to use different forms of energy.

**Word Bank**

light
heat
sound

Light, heat, and sound are three forms of energy. Write the word that matches the form of energy in each picture.

_____     _____     _____

_____     _____     _____

Energy is the ability to do work. Electricity is a form of energy that we use to do work.

These machines use electricity to produce mechanical energy. Tell what each machine does.

vacuum cleaner

food mixer

drill

toothbrush

Name something with moving parts in your house or garage that uses electricity to do work.

Anything that moves
has energy.

 Moving air has energy. If air moves fast
enough, it can make a tree bend.

Moving water has energy. Quickly
moving water can move a house!

 All moving objects have energy
of motion.

Circle the pictures below that show energy of motion.

Draw a picture of something moving through the air.

Draw a picture of something moving through water.

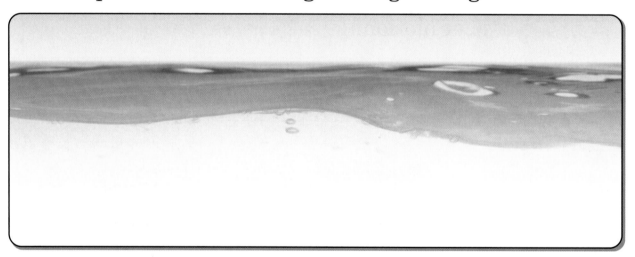

Draw a picture of something moving on land.

Moving objects have energy of motion.

Draw an arrow to show the change from stored energy to energy of motion.

Energy from the sun is stored in this ear of corn. When you eat food, your body uses the stored energy. The energy keeps you warm and gives you strength to move your body.

Gasoline is also a source of stored energy. The energy stored in gasoline makes the lawn mower move.

Energy can be stored in a battery. When the toy is turned on, the energy stored in the battery makes the toy move.

Name your favorite toy that uses batteries to move. Tell how it works.

_____

- - - - - - - - - - - - - - - - - - - - - - - - - - - - -

_____

_____

- - - - - - - - - - - - - - - - - - - - - - - - - - - - - - - - - - - - -

_____

Batteries store
energy to make the toy work.

Describe how you get to school each day. Tell where the energy comes from to get you there.

_____

- - - - - - - - - - - - - - - - - - - - - - - - - - - - -

_____

- - - - - - - - - - - - - - - - - - - - - - - - - - - - - - - - - - - - -

Gasoline stores energy to run the bus.

Name your favorite healthy food. Describe one thing you like to do with the energy you get from food.

_____

- - - - - - - - - - - - - - - - - - - - - - - - - - - - -

_____

Food stores energy that the boys need to play.

- - - - - - - - - - - - - - - - - - - - - - - - - - - - - - - - - - - - -

_____

_____

- - - - - - - - - - - - - - - - - - - - - - - - - - - - - - - - - - - - -

## Materials

ruler
rubber eraser
2 small plastic blocks

## Skills

test
observe
conclude

**Problem**     Does the amount of energy stored in an object depend on how high it is held above the ground?

**Hypothesis**  I think an object has more stored energy when it is held at a ____ height.
○ low      ○ high

**Plan**        How can you test this hypothesis?

**Experiment**  Make a beam balance using a ruler and an eraser. Place a small plastic block on one end of the balance. Move the ruler on the eraser until it is balanced.

Hold another small plastic block about 2 inches above the other end of the balance. Drop this block and observe what happens. Record what you observe on the next page.

Reset the ruler to be sure it is balanced. Now drop the block from a height of about 10 inches. Record what you observe.

**Observe and Collect Data**

Tell what happened when you dropped a block from a height of 2 inches.

_____

_____

_____

_____

_____

Tell what happened when you dropped the block from a height of 10 inches.

_____

_____

_____

_____

_____

**Conclusion**

An object has more stored energy when it is held at a ____ height.

○ low     ○ high

What do you think would happen if you dropped the block from a height of 20 inches?  Test your hypothesis!

People have used the energy in moving water and wind to do useful work.

Water from a stream or river runs over the paddles of a waterwheel and makes it turn.

The energy in the moving water travels into the wheel, through the axle of the wheel, and into the machinery of a flour mill.

**Millstone**

**Gears**

**Wheel**

Inside the mill, the energy moves through gears. It turns a large millstone that grinds wheat or barley seeds into flour to make bread.

**Flour Mill**

Windmills pump water from the ground or from the sea.

Modern wind generators produce electricity. Energy from the wind is changed into electrical energy.

A hydroelectric dam produces electricity.
Draw an arrow to show how the water flows.
Label the parts that produce and carry electricity.

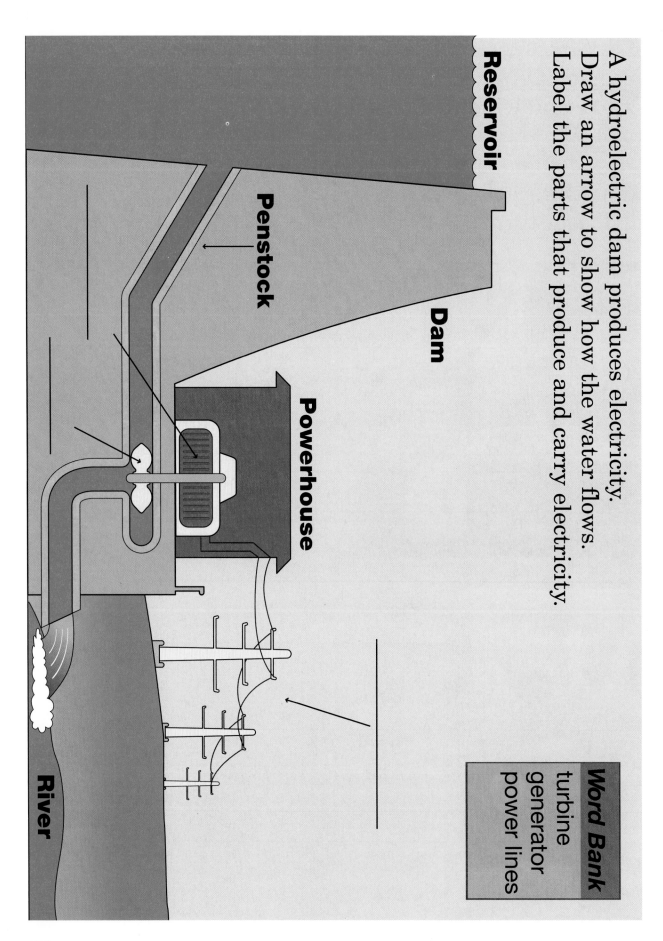

Reservoir

Penstock

Dam

Powerhouse

River

**Word Bank**
turbine
generator
power lines

**Sun**

**• Earth**

*And God said, "Let there be lights in the expanse of the sky . . . to give light on the earth." Genesis 1:14–15*

The sun is the closest star to earth. It is a ball of glowing hot gases.

The temperature in the sun's center is about 27,000,000°F.

The sun is so big, more than 100 earths would have to be lined up in a row to go from one side of the sun to the other.

The sun is 93,000,000 miles from earth. If you could drive in a car to the sun, it would take more than 150 years to get there!

Through God's design, the sun provides most of the earth's energy.

**87**

An energy chain shows how energy is stored and used by plants, animals, and people. Follow the teacher's directions to complete the energy chain.

| Joey jumping | Hamburger | Cow | Grass | Sun |
|---|---|---|---|---|
|  |  |  |  |  |

Energy from the sun can be used to make electrical power.

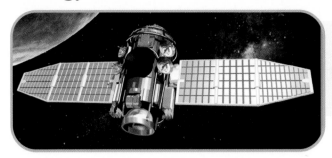

This satellite uses solar cells that change sunlight into electrical energy.

These solar collectors gather the sun's heat to drive turbines that run electrical generators.

Heat from the sun causes wind to blow that turns these wind generators.

The sun's heat forms clouds that bring rain. Water collected behind this dam is used to produce electricity.

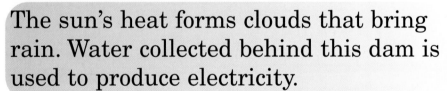

Long ago, plants were buried beneath the earth's surface. Some areas of fossilized plants under the ground became coal. The sun's energy stored in coal can be used to generate electricity.

Almost everything depends on the sun as its source of energy. Use the Word Bank to complete the sentences.

Plants use the sun's energy to make _____. By eating _____, animals get stored energy from the sun.

The steam locomotive uses heat from _____, a fossil fuel.

| Word Bank | coal | fossil | food | gasoline | plants |
|---|---|---|---|---|---|

Oil and natural gas are found underground. Gasoline is made from oil.

This truck is powered by _____, a fossil fuel that came from plants and tiny animals.

Natural gas is used to cook food and heat homes. Natural gas is a _____ fuel.

**1.** Circle the pictures that show energy of motion.

**2.** Circle the ball that has more stored energy.

**3.** Match the picture in the top row with its source of stored energy.

  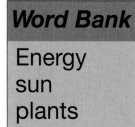

Use the Word Bank to complete each sentence.

**4.** The _____ is a ball of glowing hot gases.

**Word Bank**
Energy
sun
plants

**5.** Coal comes from fossilized _____.

**6.** _____ is the ability to do work.

**1.** Number the pictures to show the steps in the energy chain.

____1____   _____   _____   _____   _____

**2.** Circle the items that might be used to produce electricity.

solar cells         wood         water

grass         wind         coal

# ═ Journal about Energy ═

Write about the sun's energy.

_____

- - - - - - - - - - - - - - - - - - - - - - - - - - - - - - -
_____

- - - - - - - - - - - - - - - - - - - - - - - - - - - - - - -
_____

- - - - - - - - - - - - - - - - - - - - - - - - - - - - - - -
_____

- - - - - - - - - - - - - - - - - - - - - - - - - - - - - - -
_____

- - - - - - - - - - - - - - - - - - - - - - - - - - - - - - -
_____

Light enables us to see things.

# My Booklet about Light

**Name** _____

Draw an indoor picture. Show the source of light.

*God said, "Let there be light," and there was light. Genesis 1:3*

Light is a form of energy. Light makes us able to see things. God created the sun as our primary source of light.

God gave people wisdom to invent other sources of light. These help us see indoors, in dark places, and at night.

Circle the items below that make their own light.

Some things, like a light bulb or a TV, produce light energy. We are able to see the light energy with our eyes.

Where does the light energy come from in this picture?

Most things we see do not make their own light. Light travels from a source of light energy and shines on objects. Some of the light energy bounces off the objects and travels to our eyes.

What is the source of light in this picture?

The moon does not make its own light. Light from the sun shines on the moon. Light energy from the sun bounces off the moon and travels to the earth.

Draw a picture of yourself in your bedroom. Include the light or lamp in your room.

When light shines on most objects, some of the light rays bounce back, or reflect. The reflected light is what you see.

What colors do you see in this picture?

Some colors reflect more light energy and some reflect less.

The stripe on the side of the model car reflects most of the light that shines on it. It appears white.

The tires on the car absorb most of the light and reflect little back to see. They appear black.

Which person is easier to see?

Does white or black reflect more light?

A light-colored object reflects more light energy.

A dark-colored object reflects less light energy.

When light shines on a smooth, shiny surface, such as a mirror, almost all the light rays reflect off it. You see a reflection.

Circle the item that shows a reflection.

Match the picture with the best description.

Shows
a reflection

Absorbs
more light

Reflects
more light

Use the Word Bank to complete each sentence.

**Word Bank** reflect  shiny  light

Dark-colored objects absorb more _____ energy.

Light-colored objects _____ more light energy.

Smooth, _____ objects show reflections.

The girl in the picture is looking through a window. Because the glass in the window is transparent, she does not see it. She sees the trees outside.

Transparent materials allow light to pass through them. Objects can be seen clearly through transparent materials such as glass.

The apple on the table is opaque. Something that is opaque does not allow light to pass through it.

The glass in this window is transparent. What do you see through the window?

The man is opaque. You cannot see the car behind him.

Is air transparent or opaque? _____

The person behind the glass looks blurry. This glass is translucent. Something translucent allows only some light to pass through it. Objects behind it cannot be seen clearly.

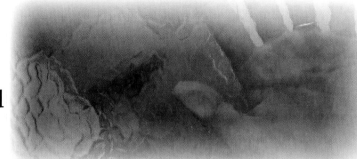

Fill in the circle next to the correct answer.
You can see the fish clearly through the water.

The water is _____.
- ○ transparent
- ○ translucent
- ○ opaque

You can see some light through the colored glass, but you cannot see objects on the other side.

The stained glass window is _____.
- ○ transparent
- ○ translucent
- ○ opaque

You cannot see what is behind the wall.

The wall is _____.
- ○ transparent
- ○ translucent
- ○ opaque

Rays of light travel
in straight lines.

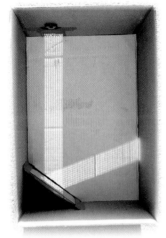

If light rays strike a mirror, they reflect.

Light rays keep traveling in straight lines
until they are blocked.

When an object blocks the path
of light, it casts a shadow. Light
rays traveling in straight lines
outline the object on the ground.

Look at the shadow on the bridge. Tell where the sun is.

Your body blocks the path of light rays and casts a shadow.

Why does your shadow look small when the sun is overhead?

Why does your shadow look very tall when the sun is low in the sky?

In each picture below, use a ruler to draw light rays shining on the giraffe and on the ground. Use a black crayon to show the giraffe's shadow on the ground.

When light enters water or glass at an angle, the light rays bend, or refract.

Lenses are found in cameras and telescopes—even in the human eye. A lens is a transparent object used to refract light rays.

When light rays pass through a curved lens, they bend toward the thickest part of the lens. In the lens below, the light rays come to a point of focus. To focus means to bring light rays to a point.

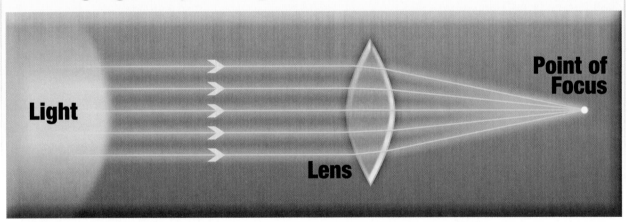

Light

Lens

Point of Focus

God created our eyes with flexible lenses. We can focus on things that are close and things that are far away.

**103**

Eyeglasses help many people to see clearly. Doctors prescribe lenses that are shaped to correct their vision.

Use the Word Bank to complete each sentence.

When light rays bounce off a mirror, they are _____.

When light rays enter a lens, they are _____.

Draw light rays that pass through the lens and come to a point of focus.

**Light**

**Lens**

**Point of Focus**

Lenses are used to focus and to magnify images. Circle the items that use lenses.

In Bible times, people used oil lamps to see at night. The lamps burned oil pressed from olives.

Candles have been used for centuries. The first candles were made from the fat of animals and from beeswax.

Coal oil and natural gas were once used to light lamps and lanterns.

The electric light bulb was invented over 100 years ago. Thomas Edison worked to make light bulbs burn brightly without burning out too quickly.

Fluorescent tubes use less energy than light bulbs.

LED flashlights use very little power. LED stands for Light-Emitting Diode.

All kinds of lamps and lights help us see. Write the number of the sentence next to the picture it matches.

1. A candle looks pretty on the dinner table.
2. A lamp can light up a room.
3. Take a lantern when you go camping.
4. A flashlight helps you see in a dark place.

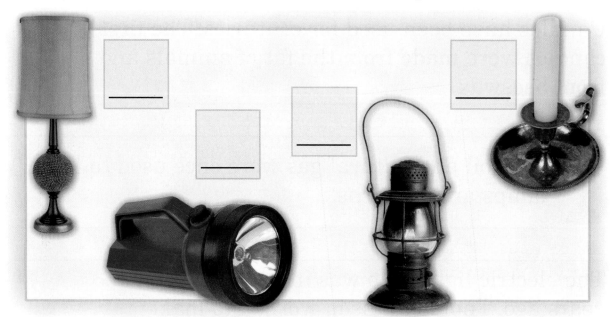

Write about something you did with a candle, a lamp, a lantern, or a flashlight.

_____

_____

_____

_____

_____

_____

_____

_____

# History Connect

When raindrops bend light rays from the sun, you can see a rainbow.

Sir Isaac Newton was a famous British scientist. He made a theory to explain rainbows. He did experiments to show that white light is really made up of many colors.

Sir Isaac Newton passed a beam of light through a prism, an angular piece of glass. The light beam was refracted as it passed through the prism. It separated into the colors of the rainbow, called a visible spectrum.

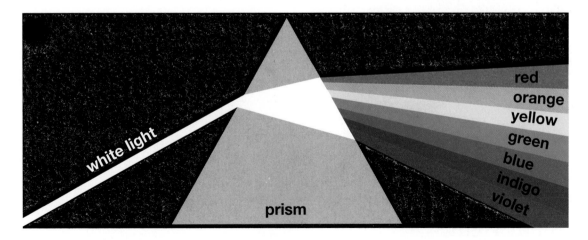

white light

prism

red
orange
yellow
green
blue
indigo
violet

Sir Isaac Newton wrote three books about his discoveries with light. In these books he wrote that the study of science leads to a knowledge of God.

Write the colors of the visible spectrum in order beginning with red.

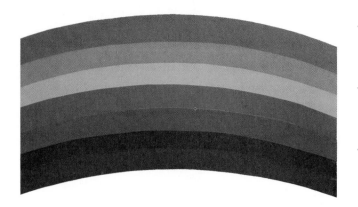

_____

_____

_____

_____

When white light strikes an object, some of the colors of the visible spectrum are absorbed and some are reflected. Your eyes see the colors that are reflected.

_____

_____

The colors of the rainbow are drawn on the color wheel at right.

What do you think will happen when the color wheel spins?

**1.** Circle the objects that make their own light.

**2.** Draw light rays shining on the tree and the ground in each picture. Color the ground black to show the tree's shadow.

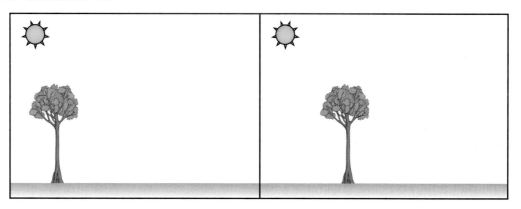

**3.** Draw light rays to show how the lens refracts the light. Draw a dot at the focus point.

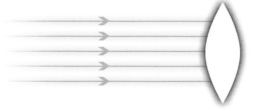

**4.** Circle the objects that use lenses.

Use crayons to color the rainbow accurately.

# Journal about Light

Write two things you have learned about light.

_____

_____

_____

_____

_____

_____

_____

_____

_____

Moving molecules produce heat.

# My Booklet about Heat

**Name** _____

Draw something in your house that makes heat.

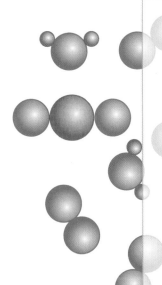

God made matter
out of tiny particles
called molecules.

Molecules are so small that
you cannot see them.

But when millions of molecules
join together,
they make the things that
you see and use everyday,
including your own body!

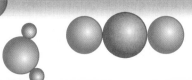

Molecules are in constant motion. Energy makes them move. Even in solid objects like this iron, molecules are moving. When you add energy to the iron, its molecules move faster and it gets hot.

When metal gets very hot, it glows red. The molecules move very fast.

When water gets very hot, it turns to steam. The water molecules escape into the air.

**113**

Molecules in a cold object move very little. As heat energy is applied, the molecules move faster.

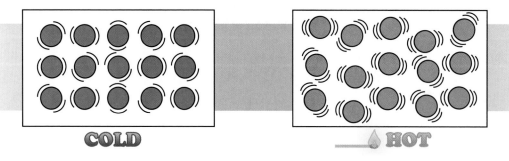

COLD          HOT

The temperature of an object measures how hot or cold it is. As energy is applied to an object, it becomes hotter. Its temperature increases.

Draw a circle around the cup of water that has the higher temperature. In which cup of water are the molecules moving faster?

Fill in the circle next to the correct answer.

Molecules _____ move.
○ never          ○ sometimes          ○ always

Molecules move _____ in cold objects.
○ faster          ○ slower

Molecules move _____ in hot objects.
○ faster          ○ slower

Heat energy moves from one place to another.

The welder is helping construct a building. Where does the heat come from? Where does it go?

To take the wrinkles out of the cloth, the woman presses it with a hot iron. Where does the heat come from? Where does it go?

When heat moves through solid objects, it is called conduction. How does heat get from the stove burner to the food in the pan?

Heat spreads through the frying pan as molecules in the metal pan move faster and bump into other molecules. The hot frying pan melts the butter.

Conduction is the way that heat travels through solid objects. Heat energy is conducted from a hot object to another object that touches it. Below, tell what each object conducts heat to.

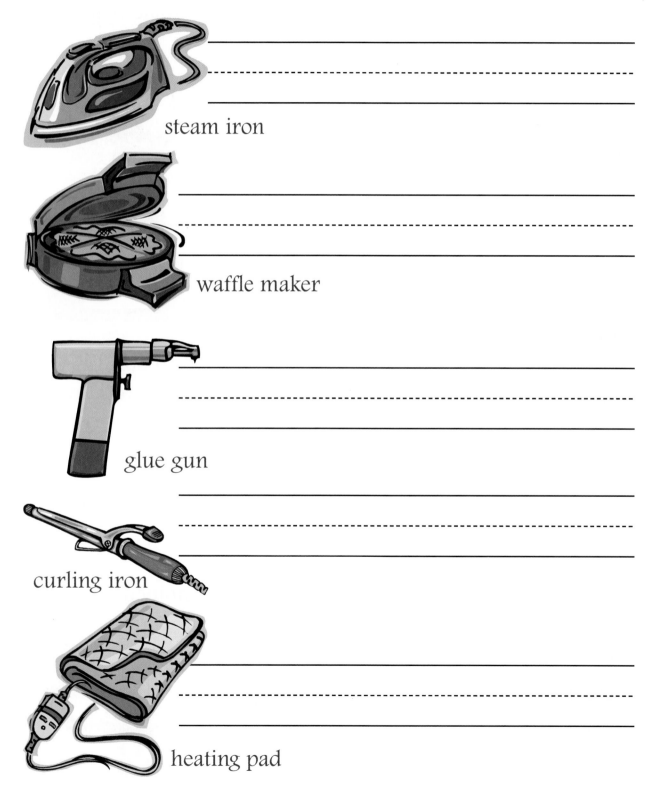

steam iron

_____
-  -  -  -  -  -  -  -  -  -  -  -  -  -  -  -  -  -  -  -  -
_____

waffle maker

_____
-  -  -  -  -  -  -  -  -  -  -  -  -  -  -  -  -  -  -  -  -
_____

glue gun

_____
-  -  -  -  -  -  -  -  -  -  -  -  -  -  -  -  -  -  -  -  -
_____

curling iron

_____
-  -  -  -  -  -  -  -  -  -  -  -  -  -  -  -  -  -  -  -  -
_____

heating pad

What do the thermos and the little girl have in common?

Both are using insulation to keep warm.

Fill in the circle to tell whether insulation is used to keep heat in or keep heat out. In some cases, insulation does both!

○ keeps heat in
○ keeps heat out

○ keeps heat in
○ keeps heat out

○ keeps heat in
○ keeps heat out

○ keeps heat in
○ keeps heat out

Conductors allow heat to pass through them readily. Metals are good conductors of heat. Their molecules are packed closely together. Heated molecules in metals bump into nearby molecules and spread heat energy quickly.

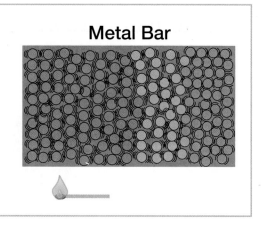

**Metal Bar**

Insulators are poor conductors of heat. Their molecules are spread far apart. When a heated molecule begins moving, there are not many other molecules nearby for it to bump into. Heat energy moves slowly through an insulator.

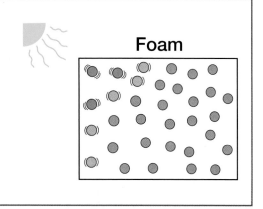

**Foam**

Heat energy moves from warmer places to colder ones. Insulation slows down the movement of heat energy.

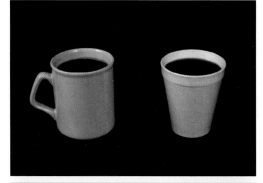

Which cup keeps the coffee hotter?
○ mug          ○ foam cup

Which cup keeps the lemonade colder?
○ plastic cup   ○ metal cup

Heat energy from the sun travels 93,000,000 miles through empty space to the earth.

How does sunshine feel on your face?

Heat energy travels through space just like light rays. You can feel the heat from a hot object, even though you are not touching it. Energy that moves through space is called radiation.

Heat from the fire radiates through the room.

These roasted chickens are kept warm by heat lamps that radiate light and heat.

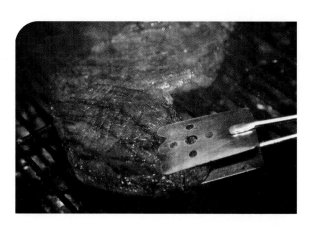

Steaks cook on a grill by heat that radiates from red-hot charcoal.

© 2005

All warm objects radiate heat energy. Some objects, like electric light bulbs, radiate enough heat that they feel hot when you put your hand close to them.

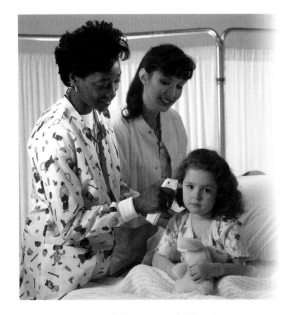

Even our bodies radiate heat. This nurse is taking the girl's temperature with an infrared ear thermometer.

The thermometer senses heat from the eardrum inside the ear.

Snack-sized pizzas are being heated in this toaster oven. Draw wavy lines from the red-hot elements to the pizzas to show the heat rays heating the food.

Different materials absorb heat differently. Dark colors absorb more heat rays than light colors.

You are wearing a light-colored sweatshirt on a cold, sunny day. Your friend is wearing the same sweatshirt in navy blue.

Who will feel warmer?

Your picnic cooler is white. Next to you, a family has a cooler that is dark green. Both coolers are sitting in the sun.

Which one will stay colder longer?

Put an X through a car that would be very hot after sitting in the sun.

Circle a car that would not be so hot.

© 2005

Rita placed two cans of water in the sun. One can is shiny. The other is painted black. The temperature of the water in both cans measured 24°C when she started the experiment.

## Temperatures

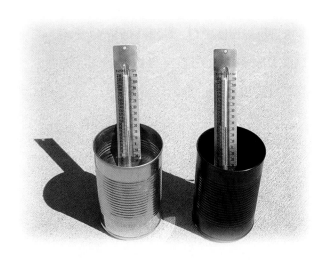

| Minutes | Shiny Can | Black Can |
|---------|-----------|-----------|
| 0 | 24°C | 24°C |
| 10 | 25°C | 26°C |
| 20 | 27°C | 29°C |
| 30 | 28°C | 32°C |
| 40 | 29°C | 34°C |
| 50 | 29°C | 35°C |
| 60 | 30°C | 36°C |

Rita measured the temperatures every ten minutes and recorded them in the table above.

Use the data from the table to finish the graph. Use dots to plot the temperatures of the black can.

Which can heated faster? Tell why.

## Heat Experiment

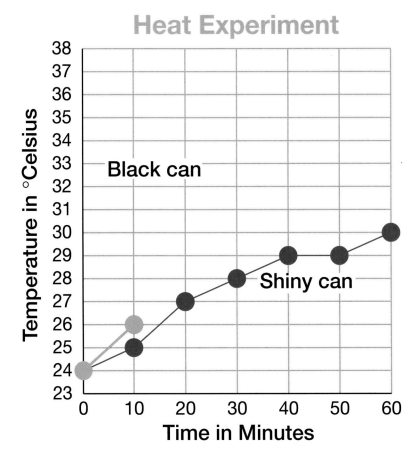

Molecules in air and water are free to move from one place to another. When air or water is heated, the molecules move faster and carry heat energy wherever they go. When molecules carry heat from one place to another in currents, it is called convection.

When heated air rises, cooler air moves in to take its place. Moving air produces winds across the earth's surface.

Some ocean currents are warm and others are cold. Ocean currents carry heat energy from warmer places to colder ones.

Have you ever stepped into a bathtub where the water was too cold or too hot? How did you make the water temperature just right?

Some foods are heated or boiled in a pot on the stove. Heated molecules of water move around inside the pot. Stirring the pot helps cook food evenly.

Many homes are warmed in winter by furnaces that blow heated air through the house.

Hot air from the furnace travels to cold parts of the house. This warms the rooms and makes them comfortable. Colder air returns to the furnace to be heated.

Furnace

This is called circulation, because the air moves through the house in a kind of circle.

Floor Vent

Draw red arrows to show hot air moving from the furnace to the bedroom. Draw blue arrows to show cold air returning to the furnace.

Heat from a barbeque grill changes raw, ground beef into a juicy hamburger.

Heat from an oven changes flour, water, sugar, and eggs into cake.

Heat changes snow to water, and liquid water to water vapor. When a liquid changes into a gas, or vapor, it evaporates.

Water molecules in ice form a rigid pattern.

When ice is heated, it melts. The heat energy breaks up the pattern of water molecules. They are free to move around in the liquid, and they move faster.

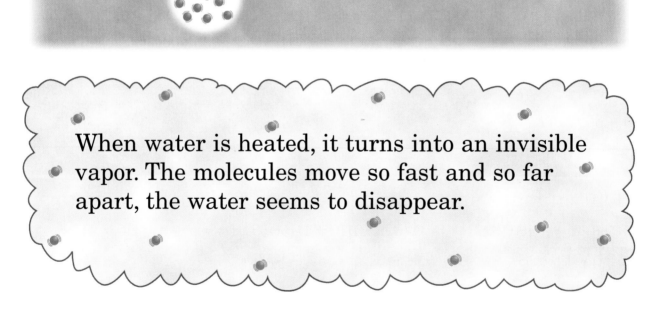

When water is heated, it turns into an invisible vapor. The molecules move so fast and so far apart, the water seems to disappear.

Fill in the circle next to the correct answer.

Molecules in _____ move faster than in liquid water.
○ ice          ○ water vapor

Molecules in ice move _____ than in liquid water.
○ faster          ○ slower

Match the picture to the type of heat.

1.

conduction

2.

radiation

3.

convection

Fill in the circle next to the correct answer.

4. _____ colors absorb more of the sun's heat.
   ○ Light          ○ Dark

5. Molecules in water move _____ than those in ice.
   ○ faster          ○ slower

6. When water is heated, it _____.
   ○ freezes          ○ evaporates          ○ radiates

Use the Word Bank to fill in the blanks.

**Word Bank**
conduction
convection
molecules
insulator
radiation

1. When the temperature rises,

_____ move faster.

2. Heat travels through solid objects by

_____ .

3. An _____ helps keep out unwanted heat.

4. Heat moves through space by_____ .

5. Bathtub water heats by_____ .

# ═Journal about Heat═

Write two things you have learned about heat.

_____

- - - - - - - - - - - - - - - - - - - - - - - - - - - - - - - - - - - -

_____

- - - - - - - - - - - - - - - - - - - - - - - - - - - - - - - - - - - -

_____

- - - - - - - - - - - - - - - - - - - - - - - - - - - - - - - - - - - -

_____

- - - - - - - - - - - - - - - - - - - - - - - - - - - - - - - - - - - -

_____

We hear with our ears.

# My Booklet about Sound and Hearing

Name _____

Draw and color a picture of your favorite thing to hear.

Draw an arrow to the body part used for each of the five senses.

see

hear

taste

smell

touch

Write the name or draw a picture.

# My favorite thing to . . .

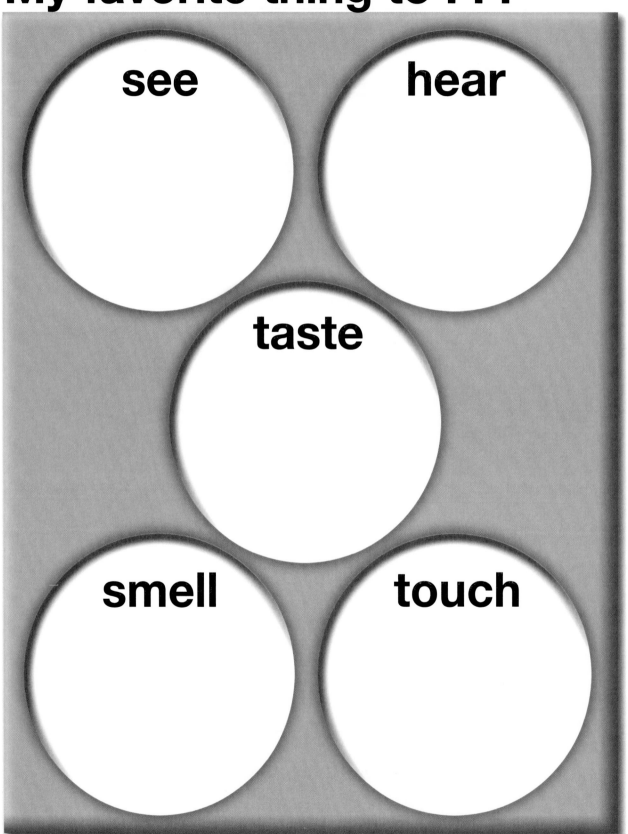

The parts of the outer ear are the external ear and the ear canal. The parts of the middle ear are the eardrum, hammer, anvil, and stirrup. The inner ear has many parts including the semi-circular canals and the cochlea.

Use the Word Bank to label the parts.

_____          _____

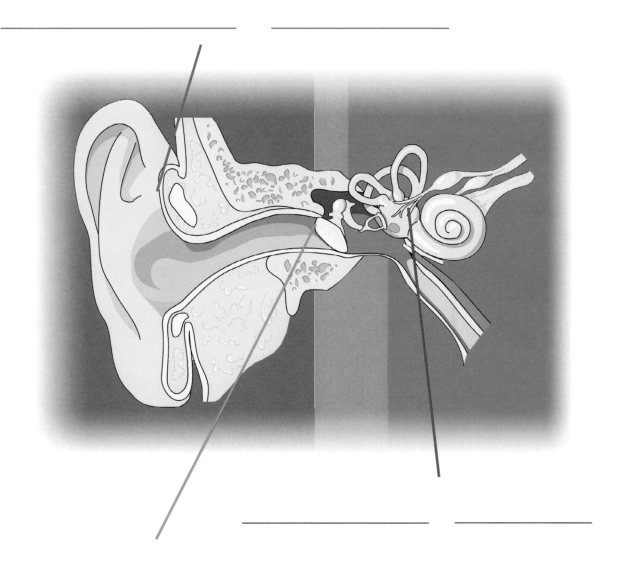

_____          _____

_____          _____

| Word Bank | | |
|---|---|---|
| middle ear | inner ear | outer ear |

Number the parts of the ear on the cross-section.

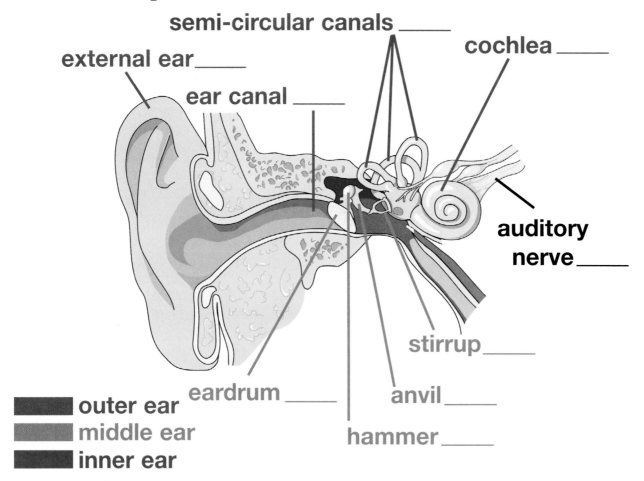

semi-circular canals _____

cochlea _____

external ear _____

ear canal _____

auditory nerve _____

stirrup _____

eardrum _____

anvil _____

hammer _____

■■■ outer ear
■■■ middle ear
■■■ inner ear

1. The hammer is a tiny bone in the middle ear.
2. The external ear is the part that we see.
3. The ear canal is a tube between the external ear and the eardrum
4. The eardrum is a tight surface like the top of a drum.
5. The cochlea is part of the inner ear that is shaped like a snail shell.
6. The auditory nerve carries the sound message to the brain.
7. The semi-circular canals are curved tubes in the inner ear that look like a half-circle.
8. The anvil is a tiny bone in the middle ear.
9. The stirrup is a tiny bone in the middle ear.

We see waves in the water. We cannot see sound waves in the air.

Sound energy from the horn makes molecules in the air vibrate. When molecules vibrate, they move back and forth. The sound moves to the ear.

Pitch is the highness or lowness of sound. When objects vibrate faster, they make a sound with a higher pitch. When objects vibrate slower, they make a sound with a lower pitch.

Write *high* or *low* under each tube.

**Shorter objects vibrate faster than longer objects.**

_____ _____

**Smaller objects vibrate faster than larger objects.**

_____ _____

When strings vibrate faster, they make a sound with a higher pitch. When strings vibrate slower, they make a sound with a lower pitch.

Shorter strings vibrate faster than longer strings.

Write *high* under the strings that make a higher pitch and *low* under the strings that make a lower pitch.

_____    _____

Write *low* on the side that makes sound with low pitch and *high* on the side that makes sound with high pitch.

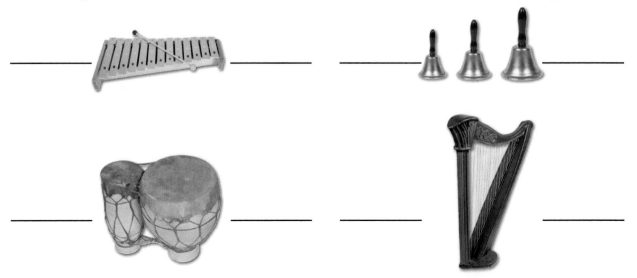

A sound wave is coming. Number the steps
1–5 in the order of hearing.

_____ brain

_____ outer ear

_____ inner ear

_____ auditory nerve

_____ middle ear

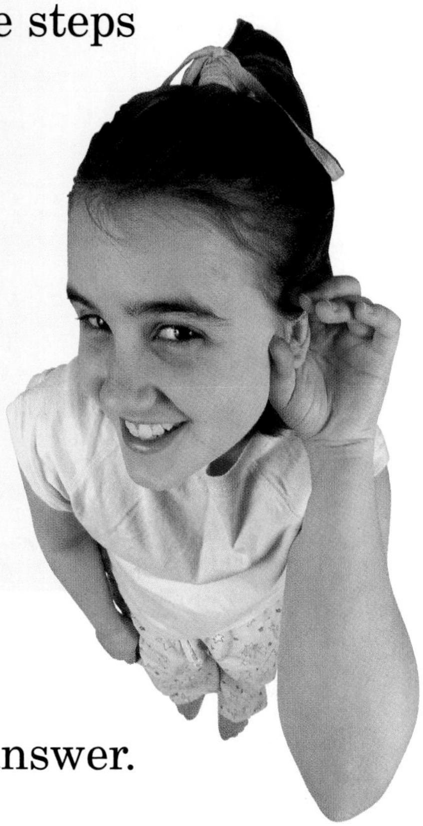

Fill in the circle next to the correct answer.

The _____ carries the sound message to
the brain.

○ auditory nerve      ○ middle ear

The _____ is guided into the ear by the
external ear.

○ middle ear      ○ sound wave

The _____ helps to understand the sound
message.

○ inner ear      ○ brain

Draw a line to match the picture to the name.

**outer ear**

**inner ear**

**middle ear**

Fill in the circle next to the correct answer.

The bones of the _____ vibrate when the
sound wave touches them.

       ○ brain           ○ middle ear

The _____ guides the sound wave into the
middle ear.

       ○ auditory nerve    ○ outer ear

The _____ makes waves that help the
nerve carry the sound message to the brain.

       ○ inner ear       ○ ear canal

People can have trouble hearing for many reasons. Sometimes a baby cannot hear when it is born. Sometimes people lose their sense of hearing because of infection or injury. Technology can help!

It is important to get regular hearing tests. Sounds are sent through special earphones. This tells doctors if a person needs help with their hearing.

Hearing aids make sounds louder and help move sound into the ear. Can you see her hearing aid? Do you have a hearing aid? Do you know someone with a hearing aid?

Some telephones make the sound louder so it is easier to hear. Others show written words instead of making sound.

This is closed captioning.

Televisions can display the words that are spoken during a show along the bottom of the screen. This is called closed captioning. Can your television do this?

Sign language is a special way of sending a message. Movements and shapes made by the hands and body mean certain things. The person who is watching knows what the actions mean and understands the message.

DEAF CHILD

Sometimes a sign will be placed next to a street where a child who cannot hear lives. How will this sign help?

It is important to take care of your ears to protect your sense of hearing.

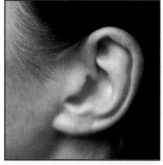

Have your ears and hearing checked often.

NEVER put anything into your ear canal. A cotton swab should be used by an adult to clean the external ear.

If your ear hurts or you have something in your ear, tell an adult. You might need a doctor to help you.

Do not listen to music that is too loud! This can cause hearing loss.

If you will be in a place that is very noisy, wear ear protection.

© 2005

Use the Word Bank to complete the sentences.

**Word Bank**

adult
protection
external
into
loud

If your ear hurts tell an _____ and maybe go to the doctor.

When there is very loud noise, wear ear _____.

Never put anything _____ your ear canal.

The _____ ear can be cleaned with a cotton swab.

Do not listen to music that is too _____.

**Help keep your ears healthy.**

**1.** Draw a line from the word to the body part.

touch

hear

see

smell

taste

Use the Word Bank to complete the sentences.

| **Word Bank** | middle | pitch | vibrate | ear canal | cochlea |

**2.** The external ear and the _____

_____ are parts of the outer ear.

**3.** The eardrum, hammer, anvil, and stirrup are parts of

the _____ ear.

**4.** The _____ is part of the inner ear.

**5.** When things _____ they make sound.

**6.** The sound of a short string has a higher

_____ than the sound of a long string.

Fill in the circle next to the correct answer.

1. Sign language lets a person who cannot hear know what someone is saying.
   ○ yes          ○ no

2. Hearing aids help make sound louder and move sound into the ear.
   ○ yes          ○ no

3. A cotton swab should be used only by an adult to clean the external ear.
   ○ yes          ○ no

# Journal about Ears and Hearing

Write two things you learned about ears and hearing.

_____

-------------------------------------------

_____

-------------------------------------------

_____

-------------------------------------------

_____

*I praise you because I am fearfully and wonderfully made;*
*your works are wonderful, I know that full well.*

*Psalm 139:14*

We use our eyes to read.

# My Booklet about Sight and Touch

**Name** _____

Color the eyes to match yours.

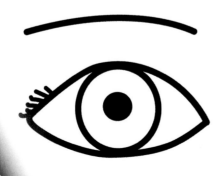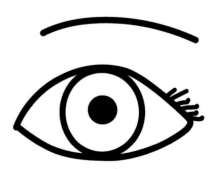

*"Holy, holy, holy is the LORD Almighty; the whole earth is full of his glory."* Isaiah 6:3

One reason God made our eyes is so that we could see His creation. We learn more about God when we observe creation.

The mountains reflect God's majesty.

The delicate insect shows God's creative skill.

Our eyes are designed with special parts to help us see. Number the parts of the eye on the drawing.

1. The cornea is a clear layer of tissue on the front of the eye.

2. The iris is the colored part of the eye.

3. The pupil controls the amount of light that enters the eye.

4. The lens focuses the light.

5. The retina turns light into a message that is sent to the brain.

6. The optic nerve carries the message to the brain.

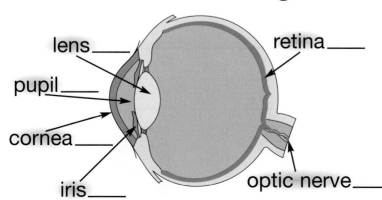

lens___
pupil___
cornea___
iris___
retina___
optic nerve___

**147**

God designed us with special eye protection.

On the face below, draw the things that protect our eyes.

Eyebrows help prevent bright overhead light from entering the eyes.

Eyelashes help keep small particles out of the eyes.

Eyelids cover the eyes to keep dust and other objects from entering the eyes.

Tears keep the eyes moist and wash out dust and dirt.

Write a sentence thanking God for your eyes.

## How do we see?

Light enters the eye through the pupil. Images are then focused by the lens onto the retina at the back of the eye. The retina turns light into a message that is sent through the optic nerve to the brain.

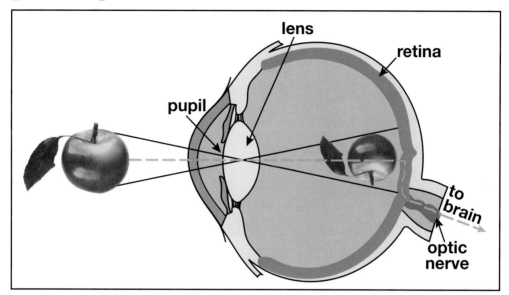

Write the pathway light takes through the eye.

_____  _____
    1                  2

→ _____  → _____
    3                  4

→ _____
       5

**Word Bank**

brain
pupil
optic nerve
lens
retina

The retina has parts that respond to light. They are called rods and cones.

Cones help us see in color. Light is always needed to see color.

Rods help us see shapes and shadows, but not color. They let us see in dim light and at night.

Being able to see color is very helpful. We use color for many things.

What does a red light mean?

_____

- - - - - - - - - - - - - - - - - - - - - - - - - - - - - - - -

_____

When people have trouble seeing, they wear glasses or contact lenses.

Many people wear glasses.

*Children wear glasses.*                    *Adults wear glasses, too.*

**Nearsighted** people can see nearby objects better than objects that are far away.

**Farsighted** people can see objects that are far away better than objects that are nearby.

Ben wears glasses.

This is what Ben sees without glasses.          This is what Ben sees with glasses.

Ben is _____.
○ nearsighted    ○ farsighted

Some people are color-blind. They have trouble seeing the difference between certain colors.

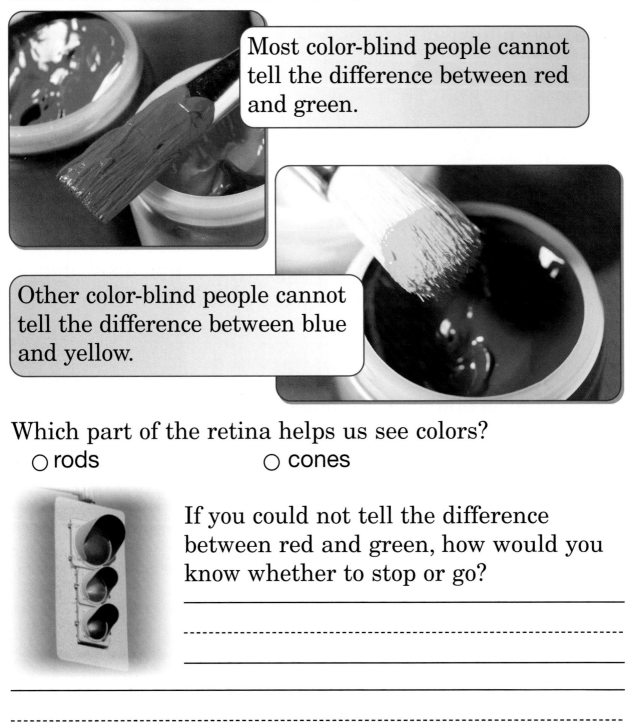

Most color-blind people cannot tell the difference between red and green.

Other color-blind people cannot tell the difference between blue and yellow.

Which part of the retina helps us see colors?

○ rods              ○ cones

If you could not tell the difference between red and green, how would you know whether to stop or go?

_____

-------------------------------------------------

_____

_____

-------------------------------------------------

_____

-------------------------------------------------

_____

# History Connect

Helen Keller was both blind and deaf.

She lived in a world of darkness and silence until her teacher, Anne Sullivan, helped her learn that everything has a name.

Helen learned how to read, write, and even speak!

She graduated from college and traveled around the world to help improve the lives of people with disabilities.

She once said, "We are never really happy until we try to brighten the lives of others."

What are some ways you can brighten the lives of others?

_____

_____

_____

_____

_____

_____

_____

Helen Keller used braille to read and write. Braille is an alphabet made of raised dots.

You may have seen braille on signs.

### The Braille Alphabet

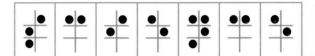

Normally, these raised dots can be touched with the fingers. They help people with blindness to read signs, books, and magazines.

What does this say?

_____ _____ _____ _____ _____ _____ _____

Can you find the letters in your name? Write your name on the blanks and then write it in braille.

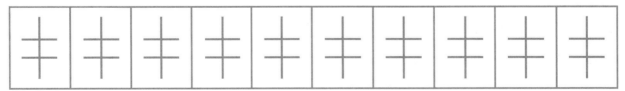

_____ _____ _____ _____ _____ _____ _____ _____ _____

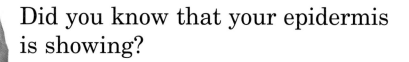

Did you know that your epidermis is showing?

The epidermis is the outer layer of your skin. God designed skin to help you in many ways.

Skin covers and protects your body from the sun's harmful rays.

Your skin releases a substance that makes skin waterproof.

Sweat glands in your skin help cool your body when it gets hot.

God loves variety. He created people with many different skin colors.

Melanin is the substance in skin that gives it its color. The more melanin you have, the darker your skin.

Look at your arm. If you could see all the layers of skin, this is what you would see. Number the parts of the skin on the drawing.

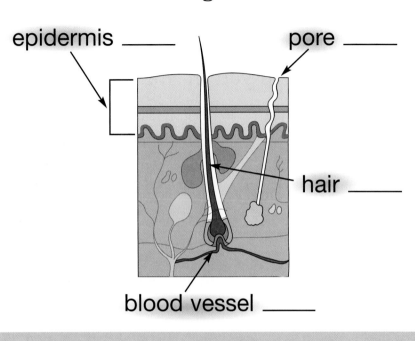

epidermis _____

pore _____

hair _____

blood vessel _____

1. Pores are tiny openings in the skin that release sweat.
2. The epidermis is the outer layer of skin.
3. Hair grows out of the skin and provides a layer of warmth to the body.
4. Blood vessels carry blood that feeds the skin and carries away wastes.

Observe the skin on your arm and hand. Draw what you see.

We feel things with our skin.

Skin contains nerves that allow us to feel many different sensations.

Use the Word Bank to complete the sentences.

| **Word Bank** | lips | feet | fingers |
| --- | --- | --- | --- |

You can use your

_____ to feel the keys when you play the piano.

You can use your

_____ to feel the warmth of a drink.

You can use your

_____ to feel the sand when you walk on the beach.

When you touch something with your skin, the nerves send a message to the brain. The brain tells you what you feel.

How does each object feel? Draw a line from the object to what your brain is telling you.

rough

wet

hot

smooth

soft

Your sense of touch helps you _____

_____

_____

## Fingerprints

Did you know that God designed every person with his or her own unique set of fingerprints?

No one has identical fingerprints, not even identical twins!

Fingerprints can be left on objects after you touch them. If you have paint or ink on your hands, you can see the prints.

Even if you cannot see a print, you may have left one with the perspiration and oils that are naturally on your fingertips.

Although every fingerprint is different, they can be classified into four types.

loop          whorl          arch          accidental

Police use fingerprints when they investigate crimes.

Fingerprints left at the scene of a crime can be used to identify suspects.

Fingerprints can also be used for security purposes. Some computers can scan a person's fingerprints before allowing access to a secure area.

Examine your fingerprints and try to classify each as either loop, whorl, arch, or accidental. Write the type on the line.

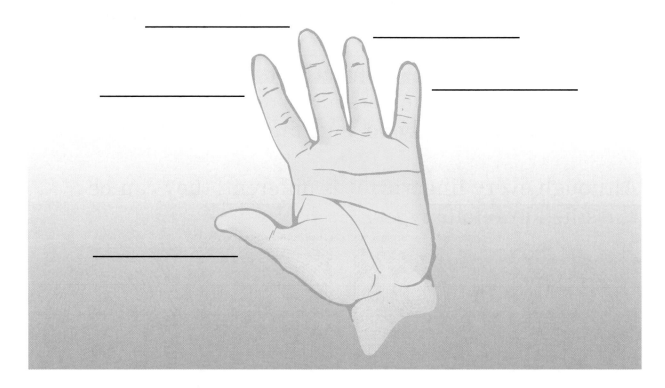

Match the healthy eye tips with the pictures.

- See your doctor for regular eye exams. Tell an adult if you have trouble seeing clearly.

- Power tools, darts, and bows and arrows can damage your eyes. Only use them with adult supervision.

- Eat a healthy diet that includes a variety of fruits and vegetables.

- Wear sunglasses to protect your eyes from the sun when you are outside.

- Be sure to wear proper eye protection when necessary.

# Match the healthy skin tips with the pictures.

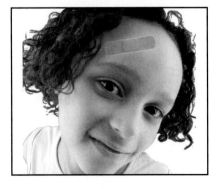

- Clean and cover cuts and scrapes to prevent infections.

- Use soap and water to clean your skin every day.

- Use sunscreen to help prevent sunburn and skin cancer.

- Wear a hat and long sleeves to protect you from the sun.

- Drink plenty of water to help your skin stay healthy.

Fill in the circle next to the correct answer.

**1.** _____ allow the eyes to see colors.

○ Rods          ○ Cones

**2.** The cornea, lens, and _____ are parts of the eye.

○ retina          ○ light          ○ whorl

**3.** To read, Helen Keller used an alphabet of raised dots called _____ .

○ keller          ○ braille          ○ dot-letters

**4.** The outer layer of skin is called the _____ .

○ melanin          ○ sweat          ○ epidermis

**5.** _____ gives the skin its color.

○ Melanin          ○ Sweat          ○ Epidermis

Use the Word Bank to label the eye.

| **Word Bank** | eyebrow | pupil | iris | eyelid |

List two ways to keep your eyes healthy.

1. _____

   - - - - - - - - - - - - - - - - - - - - - - - - - - - - - - - - - -

   _____

2. _____

   - - - - - - - - - - - - - - - - - - - - - - - - - - - - - - - - - -

   _____

List two ways to keep your skin healthy.

1. _____

   - - - - - - - - - - - - - - - - - - - - - - - - - - - - - - - - - -

   _____

2. _____

   - - - - - - - - - - - - - - - - - - - - - - - - - - - - - - - - - -

   _____

# Journal about the Eyes and Skin

Write two things you learned about your eyes and skin.

_____

- - - - - - - - - - - - - - - - - - - - - - - - - - - - - - - - - - - - - - - -

_____

- - - - - - - - - - - - - - - - - - - - - - - - - - - - - - - - - - - - - - - -

_____

- - - - - - - - - - - - - - - - - - - - - - - - - - - - - - - - - - - - - - - -

_____

- - - - - - - - - - - - - - - - - - - - - - - - - - - - - - - - - - - - - - - -

_____

Our senses of taste and smell help us enjoy our food.

# My Booklet about Taste and Smell

**Name** _____

Draw your favorite food.

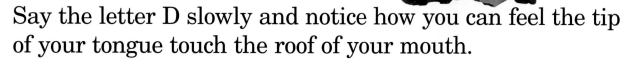

God designed our tongues to help us do many things.

Our tongues are designed to help us make certain sounds.

Say the letter D slowly and notice how you can feel the tip of your tongue touch the roof of your mouth.

Our tongues help us communicate with other people.

Our tongues also help us eat. The muscles of the tongue push food to the teeth to be chewed. The tongue muscles then move the chewed food to the back of the throat to be swallowed.

Eat a cracker and then take a drink of water. Write about how your tongue moves the food through your mouth.

_____

- - - - - - - - - - - - - - - - - - - - - - - - - - - - - -

_____

- - - - - - - - - - - - - - - - - - - - - - - - - - - - - - - - -

_____

- - - - - - - - - - - - - - - - - - - - - - - - - - - - - - - - -

_____

Did you know that the tip of the tongue is more sensitive to touch than any other body part?

Your tongue helps you taste things. The tiny bumps on your tongue contain taste buds. Your taste buds are found within these bumps.

Draw tiny bumps on the tongue and then color it.

God gave us our sense of taste so that we could enjoy the food we eat.

Taste can bring up good memories and happy emotions.

Write the name of a food that reminds you of a special time.

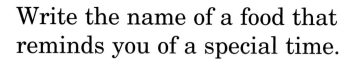

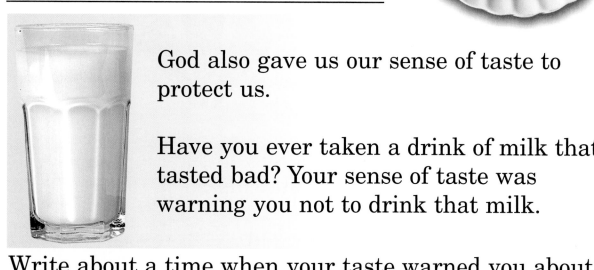

God also gave us our sense of taste to protect us.

Have you ever taken a drink of milk that tasted bad? Your sense of taste was warning you not to drink that milk.

Write about a time when your taste warned you about something.

# Tongue

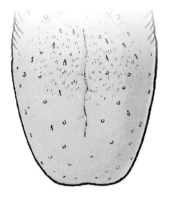

Your taste buds help you taste. They are located in the tiny bumps on your tongue.

Your taste buds send signals to your brain telling you what you are tasting.

Draw a line from the taste to the picture.

sweet          salty          bitter          sour

Did you know that cold can make your taste buds less sensitive? Try sucking on an ice cube before eating something you do not like. You will not taste it as much!

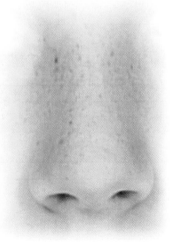

Your nose also helps your sense of taste. When you have a cold and your nose feels stuffed up, you cannot taste your food very well.

Try holding your nose and eating something. Can you taste it as well?

Gently press the end of your nose. Notice how easy it is to move and wiggle your nose. This is because part of your nose is made of cartilage. Cartilage is a strong, flexible material that is found in the body.

Circle another part of the body that is made of cartilage.

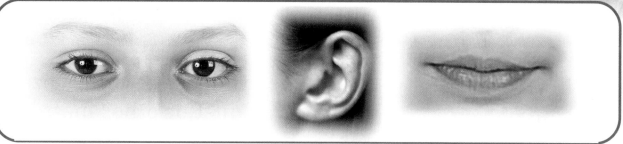

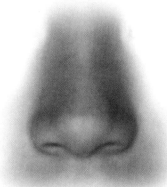

God designed our noses to help us breathe and smell.

The nose has two openings called nostrils. Air passes through these and makes its way to the lungs.

Have you ever laughed while you were drinking something and had the liquid come out of your nose? This happens because your mouth and nose are connected.

When you breathe, your nose filters the air before it gets to your lungs.

Tiny hairs and mucus in your nose help trap dust and pollen and keep them out of your lungs.

Did you know that your nose makes about a cup of mucus every day?

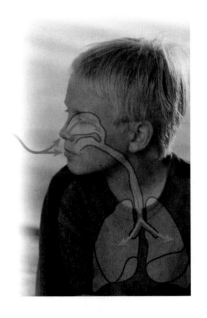

Sometimes your nose will sneeze to get rid of dust or other matter.

Some sneezes can shoot out particles at 100 miles per hour!

## Who Knows the Nose?

Circle the facts about the nose.

made of cartilage

helps us breathe

made of plastic

filters air

helps us see

has mucus

 God designed our sense of smell to help us learn things about our world.

Our sense of smell can protect us. Have you ever smelled something burning? Your sense of smell was alerting you to possible danger.

**What is your sense of smell telling you?**

Draw a line from the scent to what your sense of smell is telling you.

**If you smell...**

**Your sense of smell is telling you...**

 a skunk

• there is a fire!

 a stinky litter box

• you need a bath!

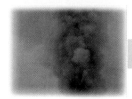 smoke

• stay away from this animal!

 body odor

• it is time to clean the litter box!

When you smell, the scent enters your nose and moves into the nasal cavity.

Nerves detect the scent and send a message to your brain telling you what you are smelling.

Your brain uses information coming from your mouth and nose to let you enjoy the flavors of the foods you eat.

Your senses of taste and smell are designed to work together. Have you noticed that food does not taste as good when you are sick and your nose is stuffy?

Draw a straight line from the hamburger to the mouth to represent taste.

Draw a squiggly line from the hamburger to the nose to represent smell.

It is important to take care of your mouth to stay healthy.

Use the Word Bank to complete the sentences.

**Word Bank** hot  sick  toothbrush

Brush your tongue with your

_____ when you brush

your teeth. This helps keep it clean.

Avoid eating or drinking extremely

_____ foods. These can burn

your tongue.

Do not drink from the same glass as

your friends. This spreads germs.

Germs are tiny living things that can

make you _____.

Stay healthy by taking care of your nose.

Match the pictures with the sentences.

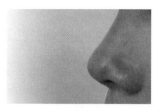

- Do not stick objects in your nose. That includes fingers!

- Avoid spreading germs by covering your mouth and nose when you sneeze. Be sure to wash your hands after you sneeze.

- When you blow your nose, use a tissue and then put it in the trash. Wash your hands afterwards to avoid spreading germs.

- Doorknobs have a lot of germs on them. Keep your hands away from your mouth, nose, and eyes after touching them.

- When you are sick, see a doctor.

 **Experiment**

### Materials
apple slices
potato slices (uncooked)

### Skills
predict
experiment

| **Problem** | Can you taste the difference between an apple and a potato without your sense of smell? |

**Hypothesis**

○ I think I will be able to taste the difference.

○ I do not think I will be able to taste the difference.

**Plan** How can you test this hypothesis?

**Experiment** Close your eyes and hold your nose. Let your partner place one of the food slices on the tip of your tongue. Remove the slice. Then have him or her place the other slice on the tip of your tongue. Remove the slice.

**Observe and Collect Data** Can you identify which is the apple and which is the potato?

Could you tell the difference between the apple and potato while you held your nose?

○ yes          ○ no

Try tasting each slice without holding your nose. Can you taste the difference?

○ yes          ○ no

**Conclusion**   I _____ taste the difference between an apple and a potato without my sense of smell.

○ could          ○ could not

God designed our sense of taste and sense of smell to work together.

The next time you eat something, hold your nose and observe how it affects the taste of your food.

Find the word in the Word Bank to complete the sentence. Write the letters of the word on the blanks. The first one has been done for you.

| **Word Bank** | Wash | taste | sour | sneeze | filter |
|---|---|---|---|---|---|
| | mucus | two | Smell | nose | Germs |

1. t a s (t) e

2. __ __ (○) __ __

3. __ __ (○) __ __ __ __

4. __ (○) __ __ __

5. __ (○) __ __

6. __ __ __ __ (○) __

1. Taste buds help you ____.

2. A lemon tastes ____.

3. Cover your nose when you ____.

4. ____ make you sick.

5. The nose makes ____.

6. Nose hairs ____ air.

7. Part of my ____ is made of cartilage.

8. My nose has ____ openings called nostrils.

9. ____ your hands often.

10. ____ and taste work together.

7. (○) __ __ __

8. __ __ (○) __

9. __ __ (○) __

10. __ __ (○) __ __ __

Thank you God for

my __ (○)(○)(○)(○)(○) __

and __ (○)(○)(○)(○) __.

© 2005

Circle the items that help keep your mouth and nose healthy.

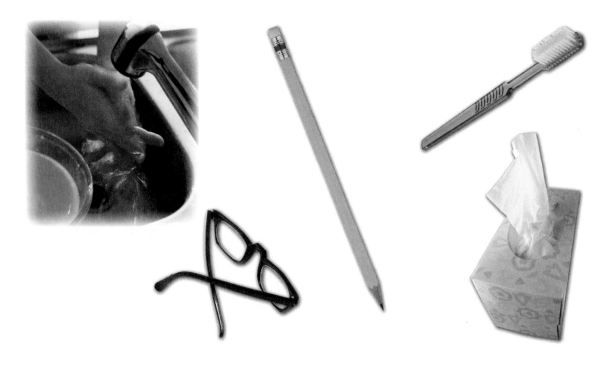

# Journal about Taste and Smell

Write two things that you learned about taste and smell.

_____

- - - - - - - - - - - - - - - - - - - - - - - - - - - - - - - - - -
_____

- - - - - - - - - - - - - - - - - - - - - - - - - - - - - - - - - -
_____

- - - - - - - - - - - - - - - - - - - - - - - - - - - - - - - - - -
_____

- - - - - - - - - - - - - - - - - - - - - - - - - - - - - - - - - -
_____

The weather affects our lives each day.

# My Booklet about Weather

**Name** _____

Draw a picture of you and a friend on a rainy day.

God's power can be seen in the weather.

Energy from the sun produces weather in the earth's atmosphere.

Label the weather in each picture.

Four things make weather: sun, land, water, and air.

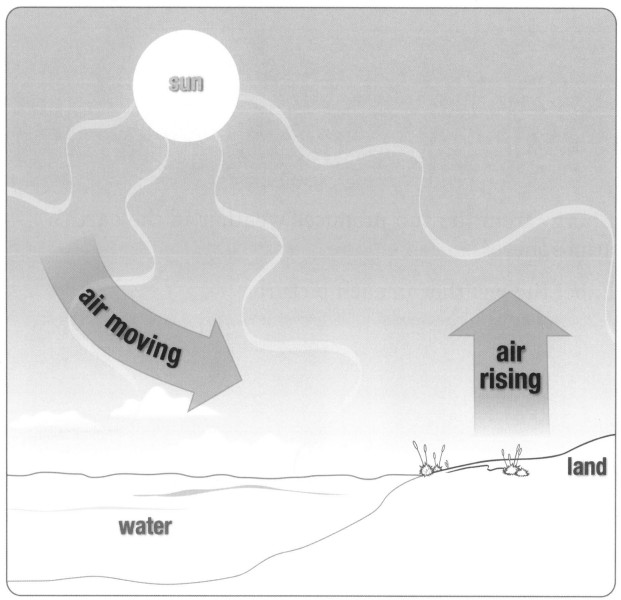

The sun's radiation heats the land and water. Color the sun yellow.

Land heats up faster than water. Air above the land rises. Color the land brown.

Cooler air over the water moves toward the land to replace the air that is rising. Color the water blue.

As the sun, land, water, and air act together, weather conditions change.

When people talk about the weather, they often say how hot or cold it is.

**Word Bank**   hot   cold

*It sure is* _____ *today!*

*Wow! It is* _____ *today!*

Temperature is the measure of how hot or cold something is.

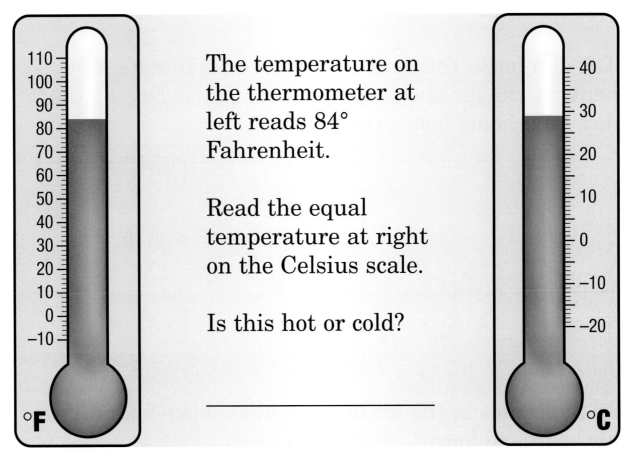

The temperature on the thermometer at left reads 84° Fahrenheit.

Read the equal temperature at right on the Celsius scale.

Is this hot or cold?

_____

°F

°C

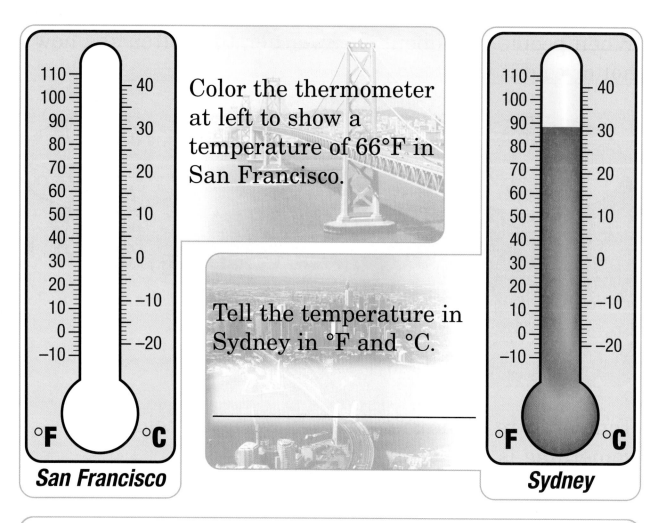

Color the thermometer at left to show a temperature of 66°F in San Francisco.

Tell the temperature in Sydney in °F and °C.

_____

**San Francisco**

**Sydney**

The sun heats the land and bodies of water. As they heat up, the air above them heats up, too. During the day, land heats faster than water.

78°F

65°F

As molecules in the air heat up, they move faster. The air begins to move.

**Evaporation** occurs when a liquid changes into a gas, or vapor.

After a rain, heat from the sun begins to warm the puddle. The puddle gets smaller and finally disappears!

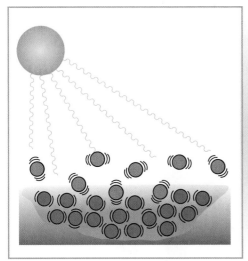

Heat energy causes water to evaporate.

As molecules get warmer, they move faster. Water molecules near the surface escape into the air.

Where does the heat come from to change the liquid water to water vapor?

Where does the heat come from to dry these clothes?

© 2005

Condensation occurs when water vapor turns back into liquid water.

Moisture inside the car has condensed on the cold window.

Water vapor in the air is condensing on the cold glass.

As molecules of water vapor touch the cold glass, they slow down, join together, and turn back into a liquid.

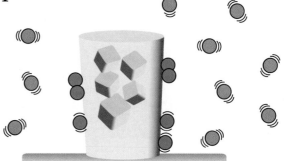

Use the Word Bank to make the sentence true.

| Word Bank | condenses   evaporates |
| --- | --- |

Water _____ when it heats up and

_____ when it cools down.

Have you ever seen dew on your lawn in the morning?

Dew is water that
condenses onto
cold surfaces.

The sun evaporates water from
bodies of water. Water vapor
goes into the air, and the air
becomes humid.

Sometimes air becomes full of water vapor. Then at night
the earth cools down, and plants and other objects on the
ground become cold. Some of the water vapor in the air
condenses on the cold plants and objects.

Draw dew on the spider web.

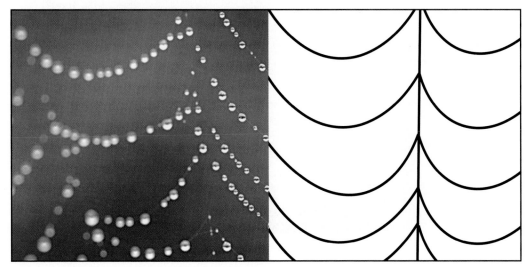

© 2005

Sometimes when water vapor condenses, fog is formed.

Fog is tiny droplets of water that condense in the air near the ground.

When air near the ground is full of water vapor, tiny droplets of water may form as fog.

Fog appears when warm, moist air passes over a colder area, such as a valley or a cold body of water.

Use a white crayon to draw fog over the cold water.

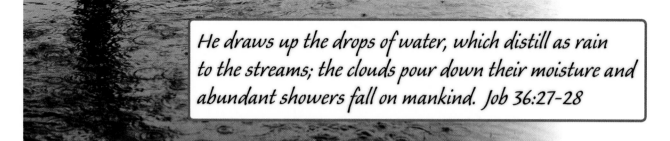

*He draws up the drops of water, which distill as rain to the streams; the clouds pour down their moisture and abundant showers fall on mankind. Job 36:27-28*

The water that God created in the beginning is the same water that is in this glass!

All the water on earth keeps going around and around in a process called the water cycle.

Water that falls from clouds as rain, snow, sleet, or hail is called precipitation.

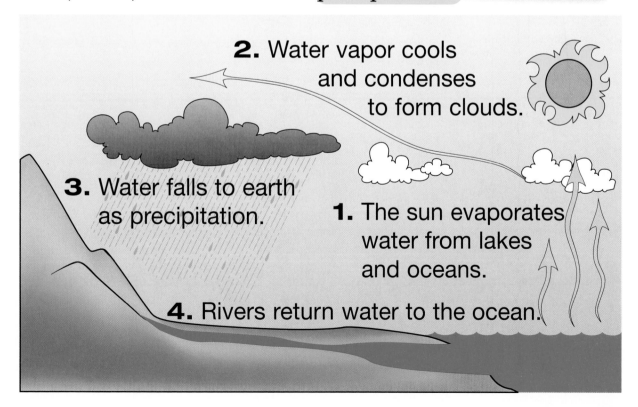

**2.** Water vapor cools and condenses to form clouds.

**3.** Water falls to earth as precipitation.

**1.** The sun evaporates water from lakes and oceans.

**4.** Rivers return water to the ocean.

© 2005

# The Water Cycle

Label the parts of the water cycle.

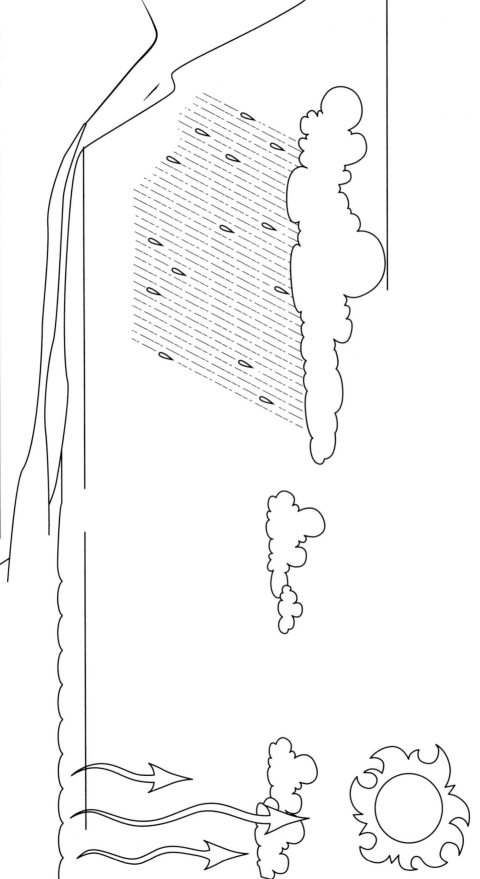

*He covers the sky with clouds; he supplies the earth with rain and makes grass grow on the hills. Psalm 147:8*

Clouds form through condensation.

As air rises and cools high in the sky, tiny water droplets form.

The water droplets attach to tiny particles of dust in the air.

These droplets are so small and light that they float in the air as clouds.

Have you ever seen a dark cloud?

Dark clouds are called nimbus clouds. Rain or snow that falls from nimbus clouds is called precipitation.

There are different types of clouds.

**Cirrus** clouds are high, wispy clouds that look like feathers or curls of hair.

**Cumulus** clouds are puffy clouds that look like cotton balls or mashed potatoes.

They usually signal good weather.

**Stratus** clouds are low, layered clouds that look like a blanket covering the sky.

Draw a line from the word to the picture it describes.

stratus

precipitation

nimbus

cumulus

cirrus

Sometimes weather conditions can be dangerous. Use the Word Bank to complete the sentences.

During a thunderstorm, electricity may build up inside _____ and cause lightning.

Super-hot lightning bolts suddenly heat the air and make an explosive sound called _____.

How would you describe the sound of thunder?

Tornadoes are strong, twisting wind storms. They are shaped like _____.

The powerful _____ of a tornado can cause much damage.

NOAA Photo Library, NOAA Central Library; OAR/ERL/National Severe Storms Laboratory (NSSL)

| **Word Bank** | clouds | funnels | thunder | winds |

Hurricanes form over the _____ and produce heavy rain, strong winds, and high waves.

Hurricanes can cause flooding and _____ to buildings and homes.

Every year, hurricanes are given names according to the letters of the alphabet, starting with A. They alternate between boys' and girls' names.

Can you think of any famous hurricanes?

Blizzards have heavy _____ and very_____ winds. Sometimes it snows so hard that you cannot see!

| **Word Bank** | damage | ocean | snow | strong |
|---|---|---|---|---|

What will the weather be like tomorrow? Ask a meteorologist.

Meteorologists observe conditions that make weather. They use this information to make forecasts.

The weather forecast helps us know what clothes to wear. What would you wear on a day when snow is predicted?

○ warm coat        ○ T-shirt

Weather information is useful to farmers.

If they know a frost is coming, they can protect their crops.

Can you think of other times when knowing the weather would be helpful?

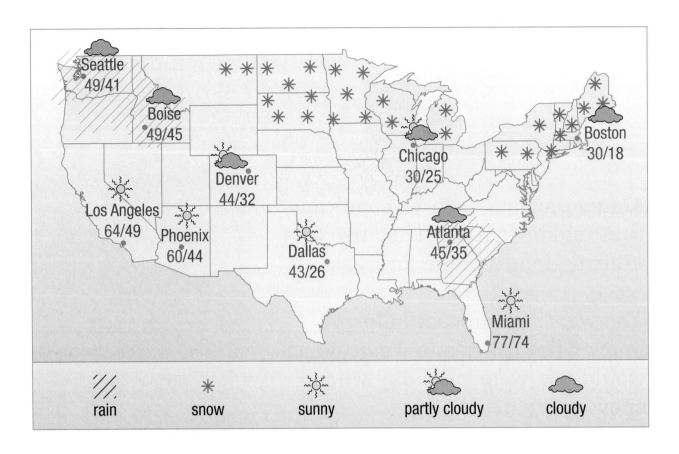

Weather Maps tell us many things.

- Temperatures
  What is the predicted high temperature in Atlanta? ____°F

- Precipitation
  What cities will have rain? _____ , _____ ,

  and _____

- Sky conditions
  What will it be like in Los Angeles?
  ○ sunny        ○ partly cloudy        ○ cloudy

Fill in the circle next to the correct answer.

1. Energy from the _____ causes weather.
   ○ land          ○ ocean          ○ sun

2. Thermometers are used to measure _____.
   ○ temperature   ○ weight         ○ length

3. Evaporation occurs when a liquid changes into
   a _____.
   ○ solid          ○ gas            ○ liquid

4. Water molecules _____ to form clouds.
   ○ evaporate      ○ fall           ○ condense

5. Tornadoes are _____ shaped clouds.
   ○ funnel         ○ square         ○ diamond

Use the Word Bank to label the water cycle.

**Word Bank**  precipitation   evaporation   condensation

## Match the word to the cloud.

cirrus

stratus

nimbus

cumulus

# =Journal about Weather=

Write two things you learned about weather.

The ocean is filled with interesting sea life.

# My Booklet about the Ocean

## Name _____

Connect the dots and color the animal found in the ocean.

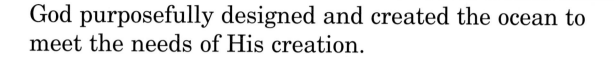

*And God said, "Let the water under the sky be gathered to one place, and let dry ground appear." And it was so. God called the dry ground "land," and the gathered waters He called "seas." Genesis 1:9-10*

God purposefully designed and created the ocean to meet the needs of His creation.

Oceanography is the study of the ocean and the plants and animals that live there. An oceanographer is a scientist who studies the ocean and the plants and animals that live there. These scientists are also learning how to make energy from ocean tides as well as removing salt from ocean water to make fresh water.

Pearls are used in jewelry people wear. Pearls are made by oysters that live in the ocean.

Salmon is one type of seafood that people eat. The ocean provides people with food and medicine that come from different types of fish and seaweed plants.

Ships are used to move people and supplies across the ocean.

© 2005

Use the Word Bank to complete each sentence.

| Word Bank | energy   seaweed   water   habitats   pearls |
|---|---|

Fresh _____ can be made from saltwater.

Food and medicine are made from _____.

Jewelry is made out of _____ that come from oysters.

Plant and animal life use the ocean for their _____.

Scientists are learning to make _____ from ocean tides.

Draw a picture of one way people use the ocean to meet their needs.

There are four major oceans. They are all connected to each other.

Use the Word Bank to label the ocean names. Color the land green and the ocean blue.

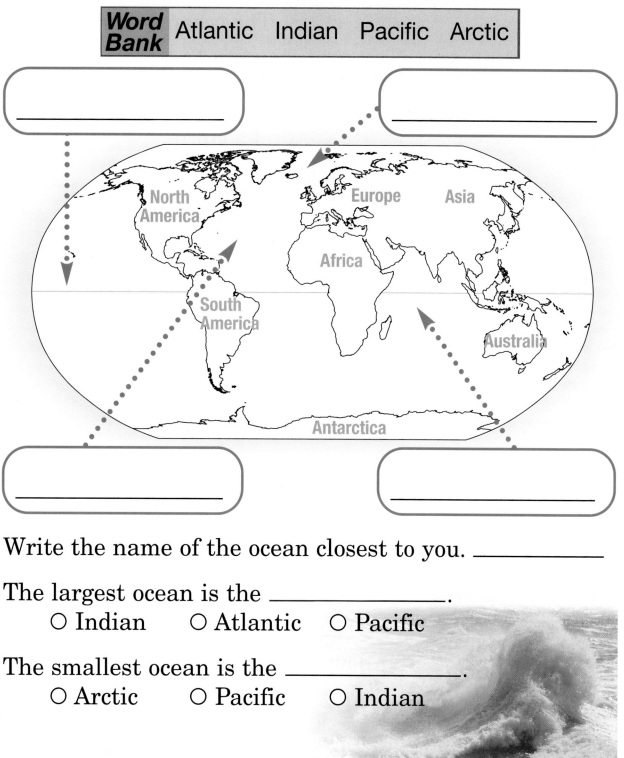

**Word Bank** Atlantic  Indian  Pacific  Arctic

Write the name of the ocean closest to you. _____

The largest ocean is the _____.

    ○ Indian    ○ Atlantic    ○ Pacific

The smallest ocean is the _____.

    ○ Arctic    ○ Pacific    ○ Indian

Use the Word Bank to finish each sentence.

| **Word Bank** | blue | warmer | colder | brown | poles |
|---|---|---|---|---|---|

The ocean water might look _____ because of a storm.

The ocean water looks _____ because the calm water reflects the blue sky.

Surface water is usually _____ because the sun shines on it.

Deeper water is usually _____ because the sun does not shine this far down.

Water at the _____ is colder than water at the equator.

**206**

### Materials

| | | |
|---|---|---|
| clear glass | water | carrot |
| measuring cup | table salt | |

### Skills

predict
observe
experiment
collect the data

**Problem**   Will a carrot float better in tap water or saltwater?

**Hypothesis**   I think the carrot will _____ in tap water.
○ sink       ○ float

I think the carrot will _____ in saltwater.
○ sink       ○ float

I think water with _____ salt will cause the carrot to float higher.
○ less       ○ more

**Plan**   How can you test these predictions?

**Experiment**  Place a carrot in a glass of tap water. Observe and draw its position in the water. Remove the carrot. Add $\frac{1}{4}$ cup of salt to the water and stir. Place the carrot back into the water. Observe and draw the carrot's position in the salty water.

**Observe and Collect Data**

Carrot in tap water.

Carrot in salty water.

**Conclusion**  The carrot _____ in the tap water.
○ sank     ○ floated

The carrot _____ in the saltwater.
○ sank     ○ floated

Some things _____ better in saltwater.
○ sink     ○ float

Write what you learned about the effects of saltwater on a carrot.

_____

---------------------------------------------------

_____
_____

---------------------------------------------------

_____
_____

---------------------------------------------------

_____

*...He commands even the winds and the water,
and they obey him. Luke 8:25*

God's power over nature can be seen in His design of ocean movement. Waves, currents and tides are three ways the ocean moves.

Use the Word Bank below to complete the sentences.

Waves are one way the _____ moves. Any movement requires energy.

When the _____ shines on the earth, the air is heated and wind begins to blow.

As the _____ blows across the ocean's surface the water moves.

This is how _____ are formed.

| Word Bank | ocean    waves    wind    sun |
| --- | --- |

© 2005

An ocean current is water that flows from one part of the ocean to another. It carries nutrients and food to ocean animals.

The tide is the daily rise and fall in the level of the ocean.

Use the Word Bank to label the pictures.

12:00pm

3:00pm

6:00pm

_____                    _____

| **Word Bank** | high tide | low tide |
| --- | --- | --- |

Match the word to the definition.

continental shelf

undersea mountain

trench

island

- a narrow underwater valley

- land that slopes into the water

- an undersea mountain whose top rises up out of the water

- a high peak of land that is underwater

The ocean floor is covered with sand, silt, and mud.

Use the Word Bank to label the parts of the ocean floor.

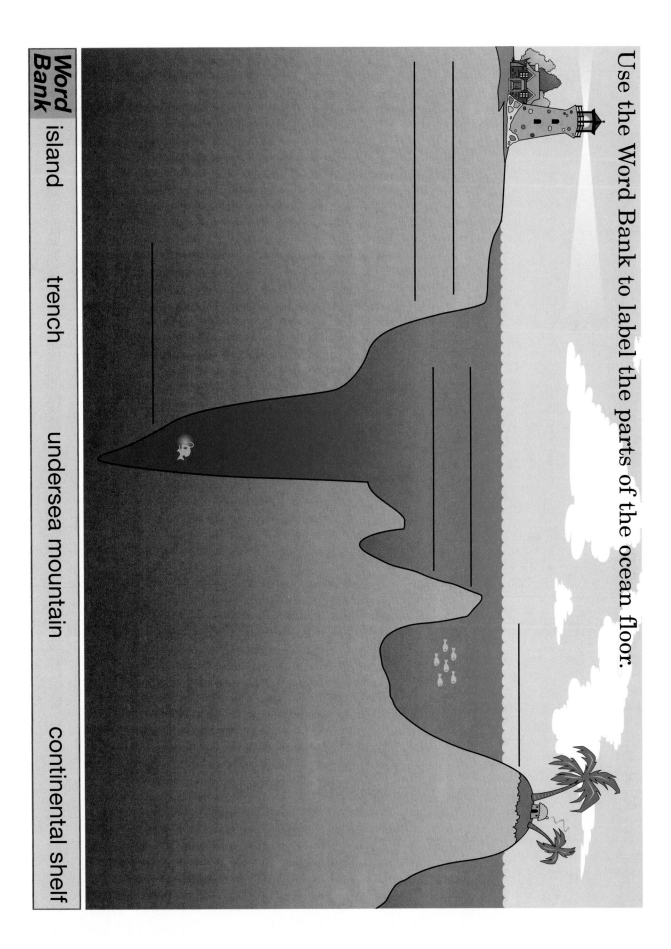

**Word Bank**

island    trench    undersea mountain    continental shelf

*There is the sea, vast and spacious, teeming with creatures beyond number—living things both large and small. Psalm 104:25*

There are three groups of ocean animals. Each lives in a different part of the ocean.

Find the animals. Write the numbers in the boxes.

Floaters are tiny plants and animals that live near the surface. They drift with the ocean currents. Find the two floaters. Write their numbers.

Two floaters are ☐ and ☐.

Free-swimmers are mammals and fish that move freely through the water.

Two free-swimmers are ☐ and ☐.

Bottom-dwellers are animals that stay on the ocean floor. Some are attached to the ocean floor, but others can move.

Two bottom-dwellers are ☐ and ☐.

# Cut out the pictures. Glue each one on the correct clue.

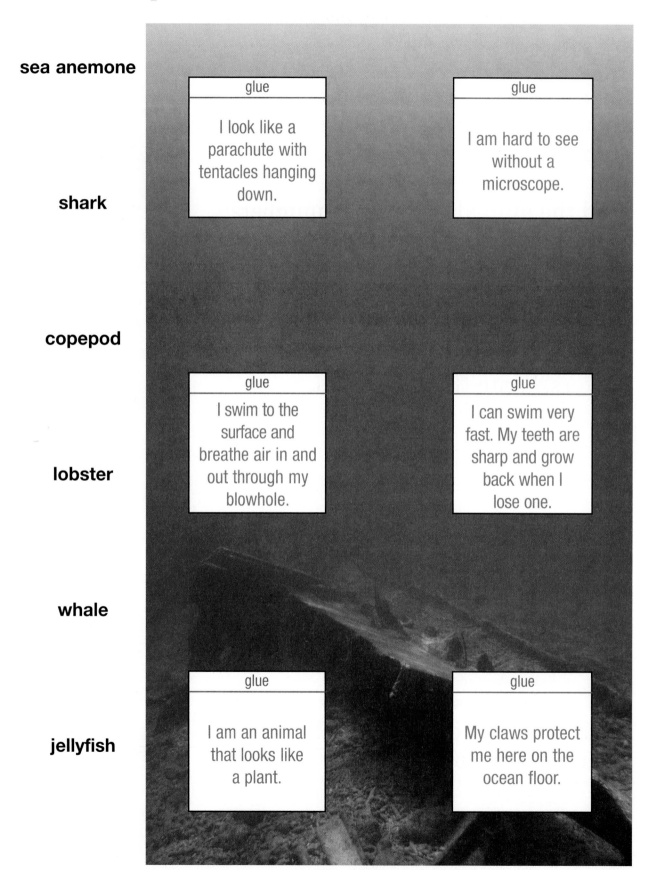

sea anemone

shark

copepod

lobster

whale

jellyfish

glue

I look like a parachute with tentacles hanging down.

glue

I am hard to see without a microscope.

glue

I swim to the surface and breathe air in and out through my blowhole.

glue

I can swim very fast. My teeth are sharp and grow back when I lose one.

glue

I am an animal that looks like a plant.

glue

My claws protect me here on the ocean floor.

A coral polyp is a tiny, tube-shaped animal that lives in the ocean. One end is attached to a hard surface. The other end has a mouth and tentacles to get food. It forms a stony, outer skeleton.

Coral reefs are an underwater habitat formed in warm, shallow water from the skeletons of millions of coral polyps. Most coral reefs are in the pink area on the map. What do you know about water near the equator?

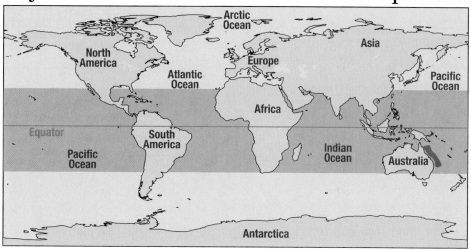

The Great Barrier Reef is the world's largest coral reef. It is located in Australia and is over 1,200 miles long. Why do you think it is called a barrier reef?

Photograph courtesy of the Great Barrier Reef Marine Park Authority

Coral reefs provide a habitat for many ocean animals.
Draw a line from the picture to the name of the animal.

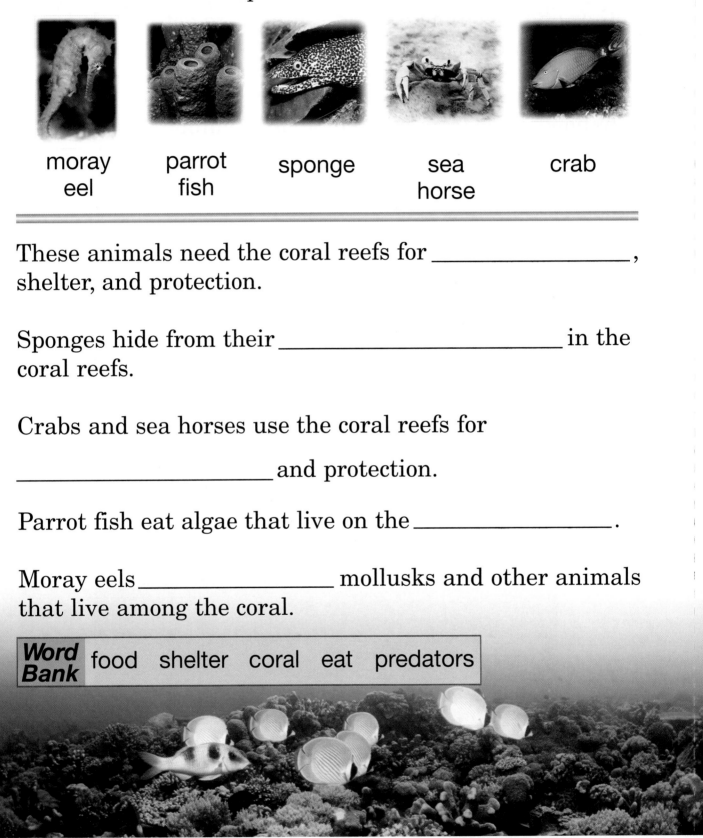

moray
eel

parrot
fish

sponge

sea
horse

crab

These animals need the coral reefs for _____,
shelter, and protection.

Sponges hide from their _____ in the
coral reefs.

Crabs and sea horses use the coral reefs for

_____ and protection.

Parrot fish eat algae that live on the _____.

Moray eels _____ mollusks and other animals
that live among the coral.

**Word Bank** food   shelter   coral   eat   predators

# Tech-Connect

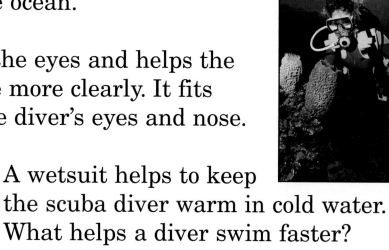

Special equipment called scuba gear helps divers explore the ocean.

A mask protects the eyes and helps the scuba diver to see more clearly. It fits tightly around the diver's eyes and nose.

A wetsuit helps to keep the scuba diver warm in cold water. What helps a diver swim faster?

A scuba diver can breathe underwater by using special breathing equipment. How are bubbles being made in the pictures?

A scuba diver can use a flashlight designed to work underwater. Why might a diver need a flashlight?

Draw something a scuba diver might see underwater.

The ocean can be explored by the use of submersible vehicles. This means that they are able to go below the water. Two types of submersibles are manned and unmanned. A manned vehicle carries people deep into the ocean. An unmanned vehicle does not carry people and is operated by remote control.

The Navy uses large, manned submarines to stay underwater for months at a time. They travel deep in the ocean.

This manned vehicle is called the *Alvin*. It was the first vehicle to explore the wreckage of the *Titanic*. It can go very deep in the ocean.

Used by permission. OAR/National Undersea Reasearch Program (NURP); Woods Hole Oceanographic Inst.

A remotely operated vehicle or ROV is used for most underwater exploration. It is an unmanned vehicle that can travel to the deepest parts of the ocean.

Used by permission. OAR/National Undersea Reasearch Program (NURP)

Write the number on the line to label the ocean floor. Write the letter in the box to label where exploration equipment is used.

**1** island
**2** trench
**3** undersea mountain
**4** continental shelf
**S** scuba diver
**M** manned vehicle
**U** unmanned vehicle

Fill in the circle next to the correct answer.

1. What is the name of the largest ocean?
   ○ Indian        ○ Pacific        ○ Atlantic

2. What does an oceanographer study?
   ○ the sky       ○ the planets    ○ the ocean

3. What name is given to stony structures formed by tiny animal skeletons?
   ○ coral reefs   ○ submersibles   ○ houses

4. What is the name of the daily rise and fall in the level of the ocean?
   ○ wave          ○ tide           ○ ocean current

Fill in the circle next to the correct answer.

1. The earth is mostly land.
   ○ yes          ○ no

2. A vehicle that explores underwater
   is a submersible vehicle.
   ○ yes          ○ no

3. Ocean currents carry water from
   one place to another.
   ○ yes          ○ no

4. Coral reefs are found in very cold water.
   ○ yes          ○ no

# Journal about the Ocean

Write about what the ocean floor looks like.

_____

_____

_____

_____

_____

_____

_____

_____

_____

_____

**220**

## A

**amphibian** A cold-blooded vertebrate that has smooth, moist skin. Its body changes form as it grows. (page 24)

**Antarctica** A polar region habitat located at the South Pole. It is mainly ice-covered land surrounded by the ocean. (page 66)

**anvil** A tiny bone of the middle ear. (page 134)

**Arctic** A polar region habitat located at the North Pole. It is mainly ice-covered ocean surrounded by frozen land. (page 65)

**auditory nerve** The nerve that carries the sound message from the ear to the brain. (page 134)

## B

**bird** A warm-blooded vertebrate that has feathers, wings, and two feet. It has a beak instead of teeth. (pages 22, 34)

**blizzard** A snowstorm with strong winds and heavy snow. (page 196)

**blood vessels** Blood vessels in the skin carry blood that feeds the skin and carries away wastes. (page 156)

**botanist** A person who studies plants. (page 4)

**botany** The study of plants. (page 4)

**bottom-dwellers** The animals that stay on the ocean floor. Some are attached to the ocean floor but others can move. (page 213)

**braille** An alphabet made of raised dots that people with blindness use to read and write. (page 154)

**c**

**camouflage**  The way animals are colored to blend with their habitat. (page 58)

**cartilage**  A strong, flexible material that is found in the body.  (page 171)

**cirrus cloud**  A high, wispy cloud that looks like feathers or curls of hair. (page 194)

**classify**  To sort into groups based on similarities and differences.  (page 22)

**cochlea**  The part of the inner ear that is shaped like a snail shell.  (page 134)

**cold-blooded**  An animal whose body temperature changes with the outside temperature.  (page 22)

**color-blind**  Not being able to see the difference between certain colors.  (page 152)

**condensation**  When water vapor turns into liquid water.  (page 188)

**conduction**  The movement of heat energy through solid objects. (page 115)

**conductor**  A material that allows heat to pass through it readily.  (page 118)

**cones (eye)**  The part of the retina that helps us see color.  (page 150)

**conifer**  A plant that makes its seeds in cones.  (page 12)

**continental shelf**  The land that slopes into the water of the ocean. (page 211)

**convection**  The movement of heat energy by currents through liquids and gases. (page 123)

**coral polyp**  A tiny, tube-shaped animal that

lives in the ocean. One end is attached to a hard surface. The other end has a mouth and tentacles to get food. It forms a stony outer surface.  (page 215)

**coral reef**  An underwater habitat formed in warm, shallow water from the skeletons of millions of coral polyps.  (page 215)

**cornea**  A clear layer of tissue on the front of the eye.  (page 147)

**cumulus cloud**  A large, puffy cloud that looks like a cotton ball.  (page 194)

 **D**

**desert**  A habitat that receives very little rainfall and has harsh temperatures. (page 63)

**dew**  Water that condenses onto cold surfaces. (page 189)

 **E**

**ear canal**  A part of the outer ear. A tube between the external ear and the eardrum.  (page 134)

**eardrum**  A part of the middle ear. A tight surface like the top of a drum. (page 134)

**endangered**  Being one of very few animals of a certain kind living.  (page 71)

**energy**  The ability to do work.  (page 78)

**epidermis**  The outer layer of skin.  (pages 155, 156)

**evaporate**  To change a liquid into a gas.  (page 125)

**evaporation**  When a liquid changes into a gas, or vapor.  (page 187)

**external ear**  A part of the outer ear. The part of the ear that we see.  (page 134)

**farsighted**  Being able to see objects that are far away better than objects that are nearby.  (page 151)

**fish**  A cold-blooded vertebrate that uses gills to breathe. Most are covered with scales and have fins to swim.  (page 22)

**floaters**  The tiny plants and animals that live near the surface of the ocean water.  (page 213)

**focus**  To bring light rays to a point or to make a clear image.  (page 103)

**fog**  Tiny droplets of water that condense in the air near the ground.  (page 190)

**food chain**  The order in which animals eat plants and other animals.  (page 56)

**forest**  A habitat that has enough rainfall for a thick growth of trees and plants. It is warm at least part of the year.  (page 57)

**free-swimmers**  The mammals and fish that move freely through the ocean water.  (page 213)

**freshwater region**  A habitat area where there is little or no salt in the water. (page 59)

**germs**  Tiny living things that can make us sick. (page 175)

**habitat**  A place where an animal lives, finds its food, and is sheltered.  (page 53)

**hair**  Hair grows out of the skin and provides a layer of warmth for the body. (page 156)

**hammer**  A tiny bone of the middle ear.  (page 134)

**hurricane** A large storm with heavy rain and strong winds that forms over warm ocean water.  (page 196)

**hypothesis** A prediction or statement that can be tested to tell if it is true. (page 41)

**inner ear** A part of the ear that has many parts including the semi-circular canals and the cochlea. (page 133)

**insulator** A material that does not conduct heat readily.  (page 118)

**invertebrate** An animal without a backbone. (page 39)

**iris** The colored part of the eye.  (page 147)

**island** An undersea mountain whose top rises up out of the water.  (page 211)

**lens (eye)** The part of the eye that focuses the light. (page 147)

**lens (light)** A transparent object used to refract and focus light rays.  (page 103)

**life cycle** The stages in the life of a plant or animal. (pages 5, 29)

**mammal** A warm-blooded vertebrate that has hair and can make milk to feed its young. It has lungs to breathe air.  (page 23)

**manned vehicle** A vehicle that carries people deep into the ocean.  (page 218)

**melanin** The substance that gives skin its color and helps protect the skin from getting burned by the sun. (page 155)

**metamorphosis** A change of form. (page 29)

**meteorologist** A scientist who observes conditions that influence weather. (page 197)

**middle ear** A part of the ear that has four main parts—the eardrum, hammer, anvil, and stirrup. (page 133)

**migrate** To travel from one place to another. (page 61)

**molecule** A very tiny particle of matter. (page 113)

**mollusk** A soft-bodied invertebrate that usually has a shell. (page 47)

**nearsighted** Being able to see nearby objects better than objects that are far away. (page 151)

**nimbus cloud** Dark rain clouds. (page 193)

**nocturnal** Describes animals that sleep during the day and are active at night. (page 63)

**observe** To watch carefully with attention to detail. (page 33)

**ocean current** The water that flows from one part of the ocean to another. (page 210)

**oceanographer** A scientist who studies the ocean and the plants and animals that live there. (page 203)

**oceanography** The study of the ocean and of the plants and animals that live there. (page 203)

**opaque** Describes materials that do not allow light to pass through. (page 99)

**optic nerve** The nerve that carries the message from the eye to the brain. (page 147)

**outer ear** A part of the ear that has two main parts—the external ear and ear canal. (page 133)

**photosynthesis** The way a plant makes food in its leaves. (page 7)

**pitch** The highness or lowness of sound. (page 135)

**polar region** A habitat with very cold temperatures. It is covered with ice and snow most of the year. (page 65)

**pollute** To make things so dirty or unclean that it is harmful to life. (page 69)

**pore** A tiny opening in the skin that releases sweat. (page 156)

**precipitation** The rain, sleet, snow, or hail that condenses and falls from clouds. (page 191)

**predator** An animal that hunts other animals for food. (page 56)

**prey** An animal that is hunted. (page 56)

**prism** An angular piece of glass used to refract light rays. (page 107)

**pupil** The opening in the center of the iris that controls the amount of light that enters the eye. (page 147)

**radiation** Energy that moves through space. (page 119)

**recycle** To make new material from old ones. (page 70)

**reduce** To use less of something. (page 70)

**reflect** To bounce back or to bounce light rays off an object. (page 97)

**refract** To bend light rays as they pass through water or glass. (page 103)

**reptile** A cold-blooded vertebrate that has dry, scaly skin. It has lungs to breathe. (page 24)

**retina** The part of the eye that turns light into a message that is sent to the brain. (page 147)

**reuse** To use something again. (page 70)

**rods** The part of the retina that helps us see shapes and shadows. (page 150)

**semi-circular canals** A part of the inner ear that is shaped like curved tubes. (page 134)

**senses** The five ways a body experiences the world around it. We see, hear, taste, smell, and touch. (page 131)

**stirrup** A tiny bone of the middle ear. (page 134)

**stratus cloud** A low, layered cloud that looks like a blanket covering the sky. (page 194)

**submersible** Being able to go below the water. (page 218)

**temperature** The measure of how hot or cold something is. (pages 114, 185)

**thunderstorm** A storm with heavy rains, strong winds, thunder, and lightning. (page 195)

**tide** The daily rise and fall in the level of the ocean. (page 210)

**tornado**  A violent, funnel-shaped windstorm that can develop in severe thunderstorms.  (page 195)

**translucent**  Describes materials that allow some light to pass through so that objects on the other side appear blurry.  (page 100)

**transparent**  Describes materials that allow light to pass through so that objects on the other side can be seen clearly.  (page 99)

**trench**  A narrow underwater valley. (page 211)

**tropical rain forest**  A habitat that receives a large amount of rain. It is warm and humid all year. (page 67)

**undersea mountain**  A high peak of land that is underwater.  (page 211)

**unique**  Being one of a kind—there is no one or nothing else that is just the same.  (page 21)

**unmanned vehicle**  A vehicle that does not carry people and is operated by remote control.  (page 218)

**vapor**  A gas.  (page 125)

**vertebrate**  An animal with a backbone.  (page 21)

**vibrate**  To move back and forth.  (page 135)

**visible spectrum**  A rainbow of colors produced when a beam of white light is refracted through a prism.  (page 107)

**warm-blooded**  An animal whose body temperature does not change much with the outside temperature. (page 22)

**water cycle** A process that continually moves water through the earth and its atmosphere. Water evaporates from the earth's surface, forms clouds, and returns to the earth as precipitation. (page 191)

**wetland** A habitat where the land is wet and soggy most of the time. (page 61)